IN A STRANGE LAND

JOHN O'DONOGHUE

IN A STRANGE LAND

" ' 'Tis gone ; the past was all a dream "
— OLD SONG

B. T. BATSFORD LTD. LONDON

© John O'Donoghue, 1958

First published, 1958

MADE AND PRINTED IN GREAT BRITAIN BY
WILLIAM CLOWES AND SONS, LIMITED, LONDON AND BECCLES
FOR THE PUBLISHERS
B. T. BATSFORD LTD.
4 FITZHARDINGE STREET, PORTMAN SQUARE, LONDON, W.I.

To
Samuel Carr
Who asked for and encouraged
the writing of this book

My thanks are due to :

Rachel Mason, for reading the manuscript and making valuable suggestions for its improvement.

Perce Amos, for helping with the technical side of CHAPTER XV, THE PLATE-LAYERS.

CONTENTS

CONTENTS

THE EMIGRANT

"BRIAN! Brian!" shouts my father. "The cows are at the gap. Get up and see after things while I go out to tie them in. The morning is fine. Don't be wasting it lying there all day."

I twist about in the blankets and look through the window at the purple mountain in front and the clear blue sky beyond.

"'Tis nice to get up in the morning," said I to myself, re-echoing the words of a popular song, "but 'tis nicer to stay in bed!" so I get myself into a more comfortable position so as to enjoy a few more minutes before getting up.

I hear a creaking sound in the yard.

"That's my father bringing in the donkey and car he's after borrowing from Barney O'Loughlin, as sure as you're there," said I in my own mind.

"Brian! Brian!" goes the voice again. "Brian, leave that!" warning me to leave the bed, and then: "What in the name of goodness is Barney after doing? He never put the kippen on to secure the gate of the rail, and I'm after losing it on the road. Get up out of that and go west to see if you can find it."

I make a move to rise and look once more through the window at the old familiar sight of the mountain that showed between the trees at my old home in Coomlaegill, but the scene changes slowly as I open my eyes. The trees become the painted curtains of the window in a little Dublin hotel, and the mountain I'm after seeing in the blinking of my waking is only the brown slated roof of a house in the opposite side of the street.

My father had been dead for nearly a year at the time, God rest him, and the voice I was after hearing was not his, but that of a neighbour, Dansel O'Grady, who was on his way to England with me. The creaking noise I had mistaken for a donkey-car coming into the yard was made by the beds of my companions lying close around me in the room as they got out to dress themselves and prepare for breakfast. Dansel was calling me to get ready with them. What a shock I was after getting, to wake up from my pleasant dream of home, and to realise that, alas, that scene of the donkey and car coming into the yard in readiness for going to the bog to draw out the turf would never again be reality for me!

I jumped out into the cold air of the cheerless room and put on my clothes in mute distress. Then, after a hurried wash, I went with the others to the dining-room where we sat at some very long tables and waited for our food to be rationed out. When it came, it consisted of two slices of bread and butter, a lonesome-looking sausage and a mug of weak and funny-tasting tea, that, I own to the devil, if we offered it to a calf in Coomlaegill long ago, we would feel so much ashamed that we could not look the same animal straight in the face for twelve months after!

This was no time for looking back, however. The boat was waiting in the harbour and I was an exile of Erin, bound to take my passage in it across the sea to England with the others; so after Dansel and I had finished our badly-tasting breakfast we went back to the room, collected our suit-cases and went off to Westland Row Station where we were to be given our travel permits and so forth.

We waited with a great crowd of anxious faces at the top of a broad stone stairway leading to the platform from which our train was to leave later on from the Harbour of O'Leary's Dhoon. I saw Dansel talking to a strange young man who seemed bewildered in his new surroundings. I went over and joined the conversation. The stranger's name was Michael Darcy and he came from Donegal. He was worried, he said, because he had left his mother alone in the home and she was a widow. I did my best to console him; saying that each of us had his own particular cross to bear.

After some time there was a movement of people towards an archway to the left and, like sheep, we followed them. They lined up at an office where each got his permit, after satisfying the officer behind the counter about his correct identity.

"Wear that on your coat," he said, as he handed a numbered piece of white circular cardboard to each man with the permit.

I looked at mine as it hung from a green string, and saw the figure 40 printed in black letters upon it.

"You lose your name as Brian now, my boy," said I to myself, like a prisoner on his way to jail, "so remember that you're 'Number Forty' from this out!"

We got into the train bound for the harbour and when we arrived I found my brother Killian, his wife and my brother Murty waiting to see me off. They had all left Kerry years ago and were living in Dublin now. Murty told me he was after finding out the part of England I was going to. It was Ely in Cambridgeshire. I was delighted at the thought of being near the famous University, because I was always interested in learning, even if I had but little chance of getting it myself.

With a load of sorrow in my heart I said good-bye and entered the customs shed where my cases were examined and chalked for admission to the boat. I moved along with the crowd that filtered slowly towards the gangway, and on my way I touched a pillar beside me with an affectionate pat and said good-bye to Ireland. Then I went on to the foot of the gangway and showed my travel permit and railway ticket to the man in uniform beside it.

"Pass on," he said, after examining the documents and me.

Before I knew where I was, or had time to shed a tear, I had picked up my belongings, gone over the gangway and into the boat. I heaved a sigh and looked around me after laying my cases on the deck. Hundreds of people, young and old, were standing about with red eyes and lonesome faces, but right above them the gulls were having the time of their lives flying to and fro, screaming, "Culing! Culay! Culing! Culay!" as they pitched themselves down for crusts of bread, or rose again to search for more. They reminded me of the sea at Annaweelogue in West Cork where I had spent so many happy days long ago with my relatives and my great friend, Kenneth O'Hara.

When all the emigrants were on board the sailors pulled in the gangway, untied the mooring ropes and got ready to move out from the quay. I waved a handkerchief and shouted farewell to my relatives. Then a great booming horn sounded. That was the signal that we were on our way. The boat heaved and the quay seemed to heave with it.

We were moving off and gradually the people on shore grew smaller and smaller until finally the boat went through the mouth of the harbour and I could see them no more.

The town of O'Leary's Dhoon nestled in at the foot of the lovely mountains in the south, Howth Head lay to the north, with the great city of Dublin sticking up its chimneys in between them in the distance. A feeling of desolation came over me as I thought of the many happy days I was after spending in that delightful country in the past, moreover in the Valley of the Vartry Waters, near Togher of the Hills in County Wicklow. A thousand memories crowded in upon my mind as the strong smell of the sea air filled my nostrils and I felt myself being drawn away from everything I loved. Would I ever see the country again?

"Good luck to Ireland, anyhow," I said, "whatever comes her way."

We had been handed a life-jacket as each of us entered the boat. Some were wearing them, others held them under their arms, and nobody kept far away from them if they were laid down, for we all feared that at any minute a bomb might drop and we would be either killed or thrown into the water. I kept looking towards the shores of Ireland until at last the grey outline of the hills faded away from my sight.

" 'Tis gone," I said, quoting the song, "the past was all a dream," and then I looked about me at my companions again.

Some were well dressed and more were wearing only threadbare clothes. I pitied these because I concluded that they were very poor. Otherwise, I thought, they would at least wear better garments at such a time as this. One of them attracted my attention in particular because the coat he wore was grey with age. Mick Joyce from Connemara was his name. He was a thin, bony, hardy-looking man of about forty years of age. He told me he crossed to England every year for work during the summer and returned again when winter was drawing near. I wondered why he never could earn enough to replace the ancient coat which looked like an old scrah you would see in a bog in the month of September.

The seagulls kept flying above us all the time and I was wondering when they might grow tired and return to Ireland, but they were like myself, going out in search of bread, God help us. I went up to a little counter and asked for a cup of tea. I was handed a sickly grey liquid. I tried to drink it but could not. If the hotel tea was bad, this was ten times worse, so I threw it over the side of the boat and returned the cup. Then I sat down and began to think of the kind old neighbours at Coomlaegill who had gathered together in our house the night before I left, to bring me presents and help me to pack whatever I wanted to take with me. I began to eat some of the rich cream cake my cousin Bridie McNamara had given me, and as I did so, I thought of the two pairs of fine thick woollen socks she was after knitting for me and which I was now wearing. All the neighbours were kind to me that night, and it made me lonely to think that I might never see them again. My soul was still in Ireland though my body was being swiftly taken over the sea to a strange land where I feared I might not be able to do the hard work expected from me, because my health was very poor at the time.

I wandered aimlessly about the boat, examining everything around me and watching the tense faces of the other passengers as well, but feeling sick and lonely, I cannot say I enjoyed the voyage.

After spending some time drinking at the bar it was only natural that some of the men should break into song.

One of them began: "My name is Patrick Sheehan and my age is thirty-four," and another finished by telling us: "That's another reason why I left old Skibbereen," while a third knocked echoes out of the rafters with: "I'll take you home again, Cathleen." I liked to hear them sing but it made me very lonely.

After about three hours on the water I looked eastwards. In front of me I saw a high rocky headland called Holy Island which looked very much like the Hill of Howth in the distance. I knew then that we were near the harbour of Holyhead, so I took my suitcases as near as possible to the side of the boat on which the gangway was expected to be laid. Hundreds of eager faces were already lined up there, looking this way and that in great excitement.

At last the boat slowed down and as it entered the harbour I noticed that the seagulls were flying in with us. I was wondering if they would fight with the English gulls when they landed, but I saw that they did not. Perhaps they were, after all, only English gulls themselves, that went backwards and forwards with the boat. If they were, they had no English accent in their cries at any rate. That put me wondering also if the dogs in England barked without a brogue.

The boat grazed against the quay and then stood still, but we had to wait about an hour before the first passenger was allowed to go through a narrow barrier where each of us was looked over by keen-eyed officials. I squeezed my cases through with the rest and I'm telling you it was no joke doing so, on account of the great crowd pushing behind and the excitement of those in front.

When we landed we were filtered through one barrier after another where we had to show our tickets and travel permits, be examined from head to toe until the officials were satisfied that we were the real people whose pictures appeared on the permits, and that all particulars connected with us were in order, so that no undesirable person might enter the country at such a dangerous time in its history. Then we came to the customs shed and put our cases on the counters to be examined by the officers.

"Anything to declare?" they asked, showing us a card with big printed lettering on it, giving a list of prohibited goods. "Any cigarettes, wines or spirits?" they chanted as they probed about among our scattered belongings.

"Anything to declare? Anything to declare?"

"I declare everything," said I as I opened my cases.

"Go ahead," said the man behind the counter making a mark like a reaping hook with a purple chalk across the ends of my cases.

I can tell you I was relieved when I took them off the bench and went towards the station platform, being led with many others wearing their number-plates on their jackets by a man from the firm which was to employ us at Ely. He directed us to a special train reserved to take us to London that evening, telling us that we had about an hour to wait so that we might have tea if we wished.

As I wandered along the platform I heard one of the porters talk, and I thought he had a Cork accent.

"Are you from Cork?" I asked when I found him alone.

He looked at me in surprise and then got a fit of laughing.

"No," he said. "I'm a Welshman, but there is a tradition that the first of my countrymen really did come from that county."

"I shouldn't be at all surprised," I said, "but this being England, I thought it strange to hear you talk like we do at home."

"This England!" he said, putting a sort of singing stress on the last syllable. "Goodness me, man, you're far from England here."

I was shocked.

"What happened then?" said I in surprise. "Did the boat go astray or change its route for some purpose?"

"Astray, your hat, indeed! That boat wouldn't go astray if it was let out on its own in the Sahara Desert."

"And is this Holyhead all the time?"

"It is indeed. You are now on Holy Island, off the coast of Anglesey, a much bigger island off the coast of North Wales. Your train must travel many miles through that island before it reaches England."

"Oh, my goodness! And is it the same moon they have in that country as we have in Ireland?" I asked, beginning to doubt if it was.

"Go on with your Irish blarney, Paddy," he said with a laugh, as he moved away to help his companions at the other side of the platform.

I thought it strange being called "Paddy" on account of my country, but it was better than being called "Forty" on account of my number!

After having my tea I got into the train with the other men wearing labels, and when it started off I kept looking out of the window at the green fields of Anglesey, surrounded with stone fences as they are in Kerry, with little farm houses nestling among them like they are in Coomlaegill. I felt lonely when I saw them.

15

When darkness came the train attendant told us to pull down all blinds so that German bombers could not see the lights. They called this idea "The Black-out." So we had to comfort ourselves in semi-darkness, for the electric light bulbs were painted blue for dimness.

We tried to sleep but could not, so we joked and laughed for a long time instead. I was particularly attracted by the witty sayings of a young man with small sore-looking eyes. He made me laugh several times, though, the dear knows, I had a hard job to keep away the lonesome feeling that held me in the hollow of its grip.

II   WORKING ON AN AERODROME

THE night seemed very long but in the end we found ourselves in the great city of London, and when we got out of the train we were marched, carrying our luggage in our hands, across a lot of streets to a big building with two tall pillars beside the porch leading to the doorway.

We expected a meal the first thing, but instead of that, we had to strip to the skin and go off to get a shower bath. I thought of Ellis Island outside New York and of all the humiliations Irish emigrants had to go through there before being admitted to continue building up the United States like their ancestors were after doing before them, as we were being led like cattle through the building.

After being allowed to dress again, we were taken to the dining-room and given mugs of evil-tasting tea and some terrible sour meat-pies. Some said they were made from jackdaws, and I felt solid sure they were; and the jackdaw in mine must have been ailing for a long time before he died, because I never found a more bitter taste in anything I ate. I enjoyed neither the tea nor the daw, and I had no sooner taken the meal than I began to feel sick.

I was glad when at last I got a chance to go to bed where, thank God, I slept soundly in spite of the hooters sounding out their warnings now and again during the night, for I was very tired after the long journey.

When I woke in the morning, however, I still felt sick, and remained so while preparing to go by train to Ely. I could enjoy nothing, and when at last we were on our way I tried to console myself with the joy of seeing the town of Cambridge, for which I had previously looked forward to so much as the great seat of learning and culture. Ely, of course, I thought, being so near, would naturally be a shining light as well.

My curse be on the gall of every jackdaw that ever found its way to make a pie in London! My head ached with a dreadful pain; and my whole frame ached as well. Finally, however, I went to the lavatory and both pie and liquid came back my gullet and out my mouth the way they entered, but in a much greater hurry. I felt much relieved, though still very sick, and remained so till I reached Ely, so that I could take no interest in anything only the chance of going to bed.

Bed, is it? Bed, did I say? Alas, I had as yet no bed to go to; but when a coach took us from the Railway Station to the Royal Air Force Camp at Witchford I checked in with the others, and each of us got a mattress and blankets to take with us to our new accommodation which consisted of a big collection of Nissen huts. The number of mine was twenty-six and I did not like it because it was twice thirteen! Dansel O'Grady and Michael Darcy were sent with me and a few more of the new-comers, but some of its beds were already in possession of others who had been there for the previous six months.

While the others went off to report their arrival to the police, I made my bed at once and got into it, because I had no other ambition in life on account of my dreadful head-ache. Looking up, I saw that the roof consisted of bare corrugated iron and I could smell the loose concrete on the floor. So this is my life in England, I sighed, for I really did feel miserable, after all my hopes of something better!

In spite of everything, however, when night came again I slept well, thank God, and woke up much improved, though still groggy, on the following morning. I got up, put on my clothes, went to the wash-house and had a quick rinse in cold water. Then I came back, picked up my knife, spoon, fork and mug which had been given to me at the camp office, and went with the others to the canteen for breakfast.

"I wonder what would the people of Gurthagreenane think of us now if they saw us," said I to Dansel O'Grady, holding up my mug, and pointing to the knife and fork sticking out of the breast pocket of my jacket.

"I have no idea, indeed," he said, laughing. "Perhaps they think we walk along like princes, with jewellery galore to shine from rings around our fingers, and watches, hanging from the ends of golden chains, for ever ticking in the velvet of our pockets; like the fellows that go back awhile among their people to show off the grandeur of their state."

"Yes," I said, "and maybe roll along the road in chromium-plated motors, where borrowed donkey-cars went rumbling with their fathers in the past."

The big dining-room had two rows of tables laid down in the same order as seats in a church, with room for the men to line up for their meals at either side along the walls and to return with their trays along the middle. The food was served through hatches from the kitchen at the far end of the room.

As I took my place in the line I looked around at my companions, and if ever there was a "raggedy regiment" they made one up. Some wore overalls, some trousers and jacket, some jerseys, and the majority wore mud-covered rubber boots as well. One or two were neatly dressed. They were the lucky ones, I thought. The lot in general looked frightfully rough. Though I pitied them I did not like their looks at all. How could I keep my place with them in the hard work that must be done in making an aerodrome? But I was in a strange land now, and I had no choice. I must make an attempt at any rate, and hope for the best. If I failed, I could go back to Ireland and perhaps die in the workhouse as so many better than me had done. Oh, I did feel terribly down

18

and out that morning, for I was still not fit for any kind of work.

I enjoyed the nice hot porridge, however, though I had to force myself to the bread, butter and tea which were not at all palatable. We were given small pieces of bacon and sausage, because these things were tightly rationed. There was hardly any sugar in the tea, and though as a liquid it was plentiful enough, I did not bother about a second helping.

Returning to the hut we put away our mugs and other fittings; then went off towards the main road to wait for the coaches which were to take us to the aerodrome some distance from the camp. I looked around me at all the strange faces, as well as at some of the ones I got to know on the journey from Ireland. There was an anxious look in most of them, though one or two cheered us up with witty sayings, as is the way with Irishmen no matter what position in life they find themselves in.

Along came the coaches, purring and hooting as they passed and re-passed each other on the road.

"This is the one we get into," said a friendly Cockney to me, as he moved towards the vehicle. "It's goin' 'o Chiambridge Reowd. The fi'm supplies the transport and we don't pay no fires."

"Is it far?" I asked, delighted at the idea of a free run in a grand coach.

"Naaw," he said, wrinkling up his face. "It's on'y round the coaneh, miatey."

I followed him into the coach, wondering how in the name of the devil I was ever going to understand what he said. He seemed to have the same trouble with me, because he lifted up his head like a cork popping out of a bottle every time I spoke, and strained his ears to grasp the meaning of my talk. Both of us laughed, because though we did not understand each other's language very clearly, we saw the point intended well enough. The others called him Cockney Jim.

After we had passed corner after corner, the coach reached the northern end of Ely at last, and I could see the towers and roof of the great cathedral in the distance. How my heart rose at the sight, and thoughts of visiting it as soon as ever I got the chance! But it soon disappeared out of sight as the coach turned sharply to the right and drove along the main road to Cambridge. Tall and stately trees grew here and there along the fences, and as I was admiring them I never knew where I was until we arrived at the entrance to the aerodrome where the coach stopped and we all got out. I went with the others through the gate and towards some wooden builders' huts where we waited for instructions.

At eight o'clock a dark-haired man came along with a key and opened the door of one of the huts. As he walked in I could see that he was dressed in a different way from the workers all round, and, over his neatly kept suit he wore a thick blue woollen coat reaching to his knees.

"Who is he?" I asked my Cockney friend, thinking that perhaps he was the owner of the firm that was going to employ me.

"Oh, that's the blinkin' time-keeper," he said. " 'E's all right, old Duff is."

The men were already in a line waiting at a little hatch which was still shut. I could feel the cold go through me, for there was a heavy frost on the ground. My feet felt like two icicles, and to add to my misery, a thick fog had come down.

There was a sudden rattle and the shutter of the hatch flew back.

The time-keeper handed each man a coppery-looking disc about the size of a ha'penny with a number on it, and a hole near the rim for hanging it up. As each of the men took his, he went off to work, and when it came to the turn of the new-comers, we were called into the hut one by one and questioned as to who we were and so forth.

"You're going to work with Angus O'Donnell," said the time-keeper to me, and before I had time to ask who Angus was, a voice from a bunch of men behind me said: "I'll see you outside," so I went out and waited.

When all the men were interviewed, the gangers came out of the hut and stood for a little while talking among themselves. Each of them then called out the names of the men given into their charge, and I was glad to see that Murthock Marshall was among those who were to work with me, because I felt he would help to pass the time with his witty sayings.

We followed Angus along the great stretches of concrete runways until he came to a very dusty-looking machine with a big basin-like wing tied by means of hinges to one side of it.

"What's that?" I asked, when I saw Angus standing beside it, talking to the old workmen.

"That's the mixer," said Murthock. "You'll soon find out all about it, as I did at Corsham last year."

"Come along now, boys," said Angus, with a pronounced North of Ireland accent. "All the morning is gone without a stroke of work being done. I don't know what some of you fellows will do for bonus this week."

"What's bonus?" I whispered to Murthock.

"Money they pay for extra hard work," he answered with a dry smile.

My heart fell. I did not feel fit for easy work that morning not to mind hard, but there was no way out of it for the present but to do my best.

A hefty young Irishman tried to undo the fastening that held up the basin when not in use, and when he failed, he gave out a string of filthy language such as I had never heard before. I did not mind a little cursing or swearing if they were done in colourful speech such as country people use in Cork and Kerry, but hearing this young man from the Island of Saints and Scholars using a filthy unprintable imported sexy adjective five times in every sentence that came out of his mouth, gave me a terrible shock.

"Hold your hand a minute, Harry," said Angus the Ganger, searching about in a little bag he carried, and taking out a hammer. "Maybe this will do the trick."

He hit the latch a few taps and loosened it.

One of the men started the engine, and when he pressed a lever, the basin came down slowly and rested on the ground, ready for filling with cement and gravel from the big heap beside it. Three men, including myself, were given shovels to do the filling, and at first the exercise comforted me a little as a safeguard against the bitter cold, but when "The Hopper," as the basin was called, rose and fell with the dull monotony of clockwork, I groaned quietly within myself as I drove the shovel through the rough stones and sand in the heap, and emptied it into the basin, shovel after shovel until it was full.

When the hopper was raised, the gravel and cement flowed gradually into a revolving pot where they were automatically mixed with water and then allowed to slide into a big waiting barrow below. The barrow was soon filled and rolled away by Harry who whistled as he went along, giving me the impression that work was a pleasure to him. As soon as he had removed his barrow, another was put in its place, and so on until hopper and mixer were empty.

The lever was pressed; down came the hopper again, and as it came down, my heart went down also, for I felt I had not the strength to keep on with the shovel work. Still, I had to continue digging in with it, thinking sadly of the time long ago when I believed I was finished with it for ever. Now, alas, I was back again to where I had left off, and with far less hope and strength left in me at forty-three years of age. I poured shovel after shovel into the vessel again, however; each shovel putting a dreadful soreness all over my limbs. It was a relief when the hopper was raised and I got a few minutes' rest. But down it came again and it had to be filled in a wild hurry each time. I was ready to drop, but I had to go on. I was by no means lazy, but quite willing to work, only that I had so little strength left in me for it.

At last we got a respite. A van came along with an urn of cocoa. I had always hated that particular drink since I had sickened myself with chocolates when I was nine years old. But I had to drink it here, for there was no choice, and I felt very thirsty.

Poor Murthock's job was lifting heavy sacks of cement, cutting them open and emptying them into the hopper; so many at a time, in proportion to the amount of gravel used. His eyes began to trouble him, for they got very sore, but he suffered on in patience while the cement dust kept blowing into them with the cold March winds. No understanding ganger would have put a man like him at such a job. But gangers were not concerned with either sore eyes or sore limbs, only with getting the job done quickly so as to get the cursed bonus for themselves and the men. Angus was not a bad fellow, but he seemed to have little or no education, so he could not be expected to bother about selection where men and jobs were concerned.

The respite was called "the tea-break," in memory, I suppose, of the days when tea was served!

After we returned to the mixer there was a change-over among the workers, and it became my turn to push the big heavy barrows of concrete. I felt I had come "out of the frying-pan into the fire," but I struggled on as best I could. As the barrow had to be rolled for part of the way over some narrow planks across a deep drain, I had a job to keep it from toppling to one side and falling in, but as if that was not bad enough, the bold Harry, who was now regulating the flow of concrete into the barrows, began to overload mine, so as to increase the output for bonus at my expense. When I objected, he released a flood of ferocious filthy language which made me drop the barrow and feel like lifting a shovel and hitting him with it. But, by God's grace, I controlled myself, until my turn came to change over again.

I managed to stay at my post for two or three days during which the fog never lifted or the frost never left the ground. Then I noticed with horror that every little scratch on my hands was festering and growing frightfully sore. I could not understand the reason for this, unless it was the change of air, or my poor physical condition; and the thought struck me also that maybe the cement dust was causing it, because it was blowing about in all directions. I had been warned by a friendly Corkman to have nothing to do with cement, because he knew I was green in the building trade.

"You can get a disease from handling it," he said, with a knowing wink and a nudge in the arm. "It is called dermatitis, and it will return every year till the day you die."

I had no doubt at all about what he said, his appeal to me seemed so earnest, and I became fully determined to avoid the danger of catching it as soon as ever I could get away from it.

I asked a fellow Irishman who had been in the country for some years if the weather was always foggy here, and he assured me that it certainly was. I got frightened out of my wits, because I felt I never could stand the climate if what he said was true. Happily for me, however, he was apparently one of those people who always get intense pleasure from telling the bad side of every story if they think their listeners will suffer from it.

By dinner-time one day poor Murthock's eyes were so clogged with cement that he had to give up work altogether from lack of sight, and go back to the camp. The ganger asked me to take his place until another man was found for the job. To avoid making a scene, I did so; saying, however, with studied emphasis, that I would not do so on the following day.

All went well for the first few hours. I watched my eyes very carefully, and though I found the cement bags very heavy, I consoled myself that I would only have to keep on lifting them until finishing time that evening. I pitied Murthock who had to stay at the job so long without complaining, and I hoped that some stronger man than either he or I might come along later on to do the work.

III   *THE REBELLION*

It was foggy and frosty still when we arrived at the site on the following morning, and as each man took his place, I stood near the hopper, ready to shovel in the gravel; a job which, the dear knows, I found it hard enough to do, and one which I would never have chosen if I could have avoided it. Now, however, I was in a strange land, God help us, and I had no other choice, for all my friends and relatives were far away across the sea beyond the Fennish bogs.

When the hopper was lowered we shovelled in the gravel, and then things came to a stand-still. The ganger looked at me, and I looked at the ganger. He moved over to where I stood, so as to make himself heard, for the mixer was making an awful noise that was anything but musical, and it seemed to be crying out for more gravel and cement.

"Get in that cement, you lazy sod," he roared at me with the voice of a sergeant-major.

I looked at him straight in the eye, said nothing, but prayed secretly to God for patience, because I felt my ration of that fine quality on the verge of running out.

"What do you mean by standing there like a silly gawk?" he asked, surprised that I did not make the customary move with excitement when a great man like him gave an order.

"Look here, Angus, my friend," said I, moving close to him in a brotherly fashion, "I obliged you yesterday when Murthock went away suffering with sore eyes. I told you frankly then that I was not going to do it to-day, for I need the sight of my eyes for a couple of other seasons, if you don't mind me telling you so."

He looked startled and puzzled, because it was so unusual for a green recruit from Ireland to dare a ganger with so cool a language in the act of earning his living from a firm by the tending of a mixer. Then he recovered his speech.

"Get in that cement at once," he said, with a haughty look in his eyes, "or I'll have you sent back to Holyhead."

That was the usual threat at the time when dealing with ignorant people. Send troublesome Irishmen back to Holyhead, Ireland and unemployment!

I looked at him and laughed.

"I have only just come from there a few days ago," I said calmly, "and you can try to send me back there if you like," for I felt that his lack of learning would prevent him sending a postal order to his mother not to mind sending me to Holyhead!

I moved away from the mixer, stood still again and folded my arms to give him the impression that I was quite unconcerned, which was, of course, the very opposite to the way I actually felt. The whole gang was held up, as no one else would volunteer to do the job I had refused.

After having a talk with the other men he went away and we all stood about stamping our feet on the ground to keep warm. Nobody reproached me, because they all seemed to understand my position. They smoked to pass the time, because none of them could think of anything else to do.

Soon, however, Angus came back, bringing with him an

Englishman called "The Walking Ganger," because he walked from gang to gang with instructions from the General Foreman. He was a really nice fellow who could listen as well as talk, and for the first time in my life I began to see what I had so often heard about—the big difference between English and Irish foremen. One was polite. The other was rude. The Walking Ganger in this case had to do his duty, however, and that was a thing I understood perfectly. He asked me to go back and put in the cement, and when I quietly, but firmly refused, he used no abusive language like the Irishman, but simply said he would have to report me to the General Foreman.

I walked away then and left them to decide matters in my absence. I did not want to worry myself any more either, because I had a nagging headache all that morning and was not anxious to add to it by any means if I could avoid doing so.

Having got out of sight of the gang at last I held council with myself as to my next move. At first I did not know what to do, but finally I decided on facing the lion in his den by going directly to the office and presenting my case in person to the General Foreman before the others had time to lodge a complaint against me.

I was attracted by many things as I went along; a great automatic mixer, seven times as big as the one I had left, and with seven times the number of men attending to it with gravel and cement; then a wonderful machine laying a whole bay of concrete without a single shovel touching it.

When I reached the office I knocked timidly at the door.

"Come in," said a voice.

I opened the door and saw a small dark curly-headed man sitting at a table with a pen in his hand.

"Well, my friend, what's the trouble?" he asked with a pleasant smile.

"Are you the General Foreman, please?" I asked.

"Yes; I'm the General Foreman," he said, scratching the side of his head, "and I wish I was somebody else! What can I do for you?"

I told him about the trouble I was in.

"That's nothing," he said, "only a storm in a tea-cup," and

then I knew I was after meeting with another nice Englishman.

He directed me to try my hand tending a bricklayer somewhere else on the site, and gave me directions where to find him.

"Thank you, Sir," said I, "and I'm sorry for troubling you."

"Don't worry," he said. "I should be quite happy if that was my only trouble."

I went out, and after a lot of wandering and searching I found the bricklayer. He too was another Englishman and from the way he received me I felt I would get on well with him. He had a helper, however, in the shape of a little ex-tailor from West Cork, and as soon as he found I was Irish and saw me looking at the job in a quiet easy way before deciding to make a start, he put on a superior air as so many of his kind are used to do when dealing with their own countrymen.

"Come on, man! Come on!" he shouted with a gruff voice, much louder than I expected from a man of his size. "Get stuck into it, man! Here's the shovel! Catch it! Don't be afraid of it, man dear! You're not in Ireland now! You're earning your living instead, and we're on bonus here, if you know what that is!"

I looked at him coldly; amazed at the cheek of a little man I had never met before. Then I calmly ignored him and looked towards the bricklayer who stood smiling in silence at the tirade one Irishman was giving to another without the formality of any other type of introduction.

"What do you think you're here for, man?" shouted the tailor, much louder than before. "This is a busy place, you know."

"Listen here, my cheeky little upstart," said I, looking him over from head to toe, "standing there like a whipping slave driver, I'm not here to take directions from you for anything!"

Then, with a friendly smile to the bricklayer, and without even touching the shovel, I turned on my heel and walked away.

"By the Rod of Moses," said I in my own mind, as another pain ran across my forehead, "this must be one of my cross days, for everything under heaven seems to take a twisting turn like a snake across my pathway since first I woke at Witchford Camp and saw the dawning light drive darkness from the Fens."

I was so worried and puzzled that I decided to leave the aerodrome altogether for the time being, so I took the road back towards the camp. As I walked along I examined the festering sores on my hands, for they were very painful. They were after getting scratched in the wild rush of work at the mixer where I was so terribly awkward and inexperienced. Wherever the skin got broken it turned septic in a short time and I was very worried about them.

On my way I met Murthock all dressed up and out for a walk. In spite of his troubles he never grumbled, but made me laugh several times with his witty sayings. We had a long conversation about the position at the mixer and he said he would never go back to it again.

"I don't blame you at all, indeed," said I, "and to tell you the plain truth, I don't know how in the name of goodness you kept at it at all as long as you did."

"Well, the way it is, Brian," he said, "the times were bad at home, so I decided to come across here to earn a few pounds to help me over the coming winter. On that account I did not like leaving the mixer but stuck at the job till I was more like a mummy dug up in the desert from the cursed dust of cement than an Irishman in exile in the sacred Isle of Ely."

My heart was full of pity for him because he could only barely peep through the constricted lids of his very sore-looking eyes.

"What do you intend to do with yourself for the rest of the day, Brian?" he asked.

"I'm going back to the camp to change my clothes in the first place," I answered, looking down at my dusty boots.

"Then," he said, "I suppose you'll walk about the village for a couple of hours like I'm after doing myself. Sorro' the hate o' good that will do you either, for I own to the devil, you might as well be walking round among the tombstones in a lonesome graveyard, for no one in Witchford will talk to you. As far as I can see, the same people would grudge the time o' day to Columbkille himself if he came along to walk the streets with seven angels spreading carpets for the comfort of his feet."

"What is wrong with them at all, Murthock?" I asked, for I too had noticed that they had but little inclination to even say the day was fine, not to mind to add a brightness to its light with conversation.

"That's their nature, man," he answered with a frown. "They want nobody from the outside world coming in to live amongst them, and they've always been like that in this part of the world as far as I can gather from the people that have knowledge of their ways."

"Well, I'm blest o' God!" said I. "The time of day costs nothing, and we all pass through the world only once."

"Yes, Brian, my boy," he said, taking out a handkerchief to wipe his eyes. "I agree with you there, but we must remember there's a war going on, and too much talk means trouble sometimes."

"Aren't we here to help them by building this aerodrome," I said, "so why should they be cool to us as if we're doing them harm?"

"Well, you see, they can look at things in two ways," he said, putting the handkerchief back into his pocket. "In one way we may help them by building up defences; in another, cause them trouble if the Germans find it out, and send death and ruin among them in the form of a bomb."

"I hadn't thought of that, indeed," I said, "but even if I had, I think they have but little reason to put blame on us for things we cannot help; and I can't see how 'Good Morning' or 'Good Evening' could bring damning to their souls."

"Well, you know," he said, "they can't change their nature any more than you or I can change a heap of ashes to a pewter pint of porter."

"I suppose you're right, Murthock," said I, "but the puzzle is to me as big as ever."

"Why then," he said, "if none of them ever said as much as 'Have you a mouth on you?' to either you or me, I'm told there is a lot of good people among them when acquaintance thaws them out."

"I hope you're right there, Murthock," said I, "but from

29

the look of things at present, I'm afraid we'll all be gone before the icing leaves them."

"God help us, that's the way with us, indeed," he said, looking sadly up into the sky. "We're only like the birds of passage that are with them in the summer, and that fly away to other countries when the leaves begin to fall."

"I think I'll move off now," said I. "and shake the dust of cement from my overalls and boots before changing into clothes I only wear on Sundays."

"May the shaking take the troubles of the world from you too," he said as we parted, "and the lifting of the burden give a lightness to your feet."

IV   *ELY*

BACK at the camp I found everything extremely quiet. All the men were away at work except a few stragglers here and there. When I went into the hut, I found an Irishman tidying up the place and keeping an eye on the property of the residents. After explaining my return to him, I changed into my Sunday clothes, went out and walked along the road through the village.

I was admiring the little thatched houses, and as they made me feel like being back again in Kerry, I naturally expected the people who lived in them to be of the same friendly character as those at home. Seeing a middle-aged man coming out of one of them I went towards him and bid him good day in the fashion of Ireland. He turned a sour face to me, muttered something which I could not understand, then went back into his house and shut the door as a man might do when he sees a mad dog.

"The Lord save us," said I in my own mind, "maybe 'tis the man himself that's mad and not the dog," because I knew that mad people are sometimes fond of keeping their minds to themselves.

Making allowances for this poor man, however, I went along cheerfully to the next thatched house. Seeing a woman going in there with a bucket in her hand I said "Good morning" in as pleasant a way as I could manage, in spite of my nagging headache; but instead of the usual answer she looked at me vaguely and seemed lost for words with the height of surprise at hearing my voice at all. She just nodded rather doubtfully and went into the house without a word.

I was beginning to think I must look like the mad hatter, so I began to examine myself from head to foot. There was nothing wrong with my clothes as far as I could see. I put up my hand to search my head in case I might be wearing a woman's hat unknown to myself, but there was nothing there.

"By the hoakey-poakey," said I to myself, "this looks funny. I must be very sick, I'm thinking. What is wrong with me at all? There's nothing on my head, and my critics always said there was nothing in it either! What is up with me at all? Am I dreaming?" and I pinched myself with a pin on the cheek to make sure I was not asleep. Even then I could not be sure, for I had often dreamt of puttings things to the same test in a very dream itself! So what was I to do?

Being quite willing to admit that it might be my own fault after all, I went on a little further and chanced my tongue with a little child who was playing with a dog on the footpath. But the minute she heard my voice, she too put on a worried look and moved away for safety towards the door of her house.

There was a little public house near me so I decided on trying my luck there by buying a bottle of lemonade. I did not know that the opening hours were different to what they are in Ireland, where the public houses are open all day until about ten o'clock at night; so I knocked at the door. A little old woman opened it. To my great surprise she started to talk at once in quite a friendly fashion after asking me what I wanted; but her whole speech consisted of a sermon about the rough men who came in to her house to make trouble. I could understand that very well because most of her customers were those working on the aerodrome. She went on and on so that in the end I was thinking that perhaps the village had appointed her as official talker to unwanted strangers, so as to make up for their own great lack in that respect. An ambassador for the dumb she seemed to me as I looked around me for the usual bar with rows and rows of bottles on the shelves behind it. I looked in vain. There was no such thing in the place, and only for seeing her name on the outside as one licensed to sell drink, I could easily mistake her for being either running a shebeen without the king's permission or an office of information for the benefit of all. However, probably seeing the look of amazement on my face, she suddenly changed the conversation from the rough customers to the immediate cause of my visit. That was a great relief to me, because I was beginning to wonder whether it was not better after all to meet seven silent people in a strange place than one talkative woman!

"You want a lemonade, then," she said, turning towards some steps at the back of the landing. "You want a lemonade. Well, if you want a lemonade, I'll give you a lemonade," and the poor old creature began to walk with faltering steps to the back. I followed her down the stairs like a dog on a lead, thinking that perhaps the public bar was in the basement. I had arrived at the stage where nothing would surprise me. The English are a queer people, you know. They taunt us with keepings pigs in parlours in Ireland, but upon my soul and conscience, I'm telling you no word of a lie, I saw them keep horses upstairs in Scotland Yard myself! When we arrived below, however, there was nothing to be seen only a bare room with a few barrels resting on trestles. She took a bottle of lemonade from a cupboard and, still talking, took it upstairs to a room on the left of the street door. She put the bottle on a little table beside the window, went searching for an opener, brought it back and removed the stopper. After she had brought me a glass, I poured out the lemonade, drank it, said good-bye and left the house.

Then I turned my eyes towards Ely, passing by the aerodrome on my way. Looking in, I saw the Royal Air Force lorries rolling about in all directions with loads of gravel, and hundreds of men working all over the place. It was a strange sight; great machinery levelling hedges; bull-dozers pushing earth and stones from heights into hollows; dumpers taking rubbish from one end of the place to the other; mixers working here and there; the whole place a great hive of industry.

Stretching away to the horizon in all directions were the dreary fens with not as much as a single hill among them, only some very fine tall trees dotting the countryside and helping to break the drab monotony of the scene. When I looked west I thought of Ireland; Kerry in particular, with its deep blue mountains, golden sunsets and friendly people.

I moved along and soon the great towers of Ely Cathedral came into view like the funnels of a ship on the ocean. As I entered the town I was delighted to see the first lovely spring blossoms appearing on some almond trees in an ornamental green, and after standing for some time to admire their beauty I made my way towards the Cathedral which I intended to explore as a form of recreation. The sight enraptured me. A vast grey stone building from the Middle Ages stood in majesty before me, mellowed by the rains, winds and dust of centuries. Its massive towers and splendid architecture brought a world of wonder to my soul. It was a noble thing to see. I feasted my eyes on every window, turret and piece of ornamental figuring, going round and round the great building until I thought I had grasped at least a synopsis of its main features on the outside.

Then I went into the Galilee Porch, the finest of its kind in the world. The hand of time had worn away the lower ends of the slender marble pillars which stood in rows along its sides. Passing through a wicket, I stood in awe before the magnificent nave with its massive white pillars and arches, as well as a beautifully-painted ceiling far above my head. I had never before seen the inside of any cathedral more cheerful-looking. There were none of the usual gloomy shadows in this blissfully-delightful building.

I bought a guide-book from one of the stalls and forgot that I was in the heart of the dreary fens as I moved along from one pillar to another, examining everything until I came under the lights of the glorious octagon separating the nave from the choir. I sat on a bench and turned up my eyes to view the grandeur of the world wonder above me. It was a sight I could never forget. Eight great pillars soared to the heavens and branched out above to join each other in a most intricate fan-vaulting which in turn held up a vast lantern of splendid stained-glass windows at the top. How in the name of all the saints was it ever put up without the help of modern machinery? What great artist planned it? How did he ever think it out?

I looked at the guide book. The octagon, it stated, was designed and built by Alan de Walsingham, and the site of his grave was marked by a big flagstone in the nave.

I got up and went to see it. A fancy rope attached to some paling surrounded it, and a notice hanging on one end said: "Alan de Walsingham, flower of Craftsmen." Never, said I in my own mind, was a title more justly deserved.

The choir too was lovely beyond measure. The stalls were decorated with the most exquisite carving of angels, saints, monks, birds, beasts and fishes, while the canopies overhead were equally delightful. The beautiful fan-vaulted ceiling had lovely coloured bosses intermingling with the intricacy of the design which was a dream of glory in itself. All around me, like a forest of great branching trees, stood the pillars with their splendid mouldings, holding up the arches of both the choir and aisles, with the lovely coloured windows giving the grandeur of a Kerry sunset to the whole enrapturing scene.

I looked about me in all directions, feeling lost for ever in the dazzling beauty of it all. I walked up and down the choir, examining as much as I could, and wondering how in the name of goodness the hand of man could do it all with such delightful harmony. Then I turned into the north choir aisle and saw the little chantry chapel of Bishop Alcock, the founder of Jesus College, Cambridge. Many of its delicately-cut white stone figures were shamefully defaced during the religious troubles of the seventeenth century. On the south choir aisle I saw the chapel of Bishop West, another delightful work of art.

Going on towards the Lady Chapel, as I looked all over the scene before me, I said to myself, that never before had I seen a more magnificent building. Glancing at the backs of some of the statues and other decorations, I noticed that the carving was done there with the same delicate care as if it had been the front. How easy it must have been for an evil-minded, ignorant mob to destroy in a short time what mighty artists had done with such loving care and skill before the great upheaval gave the power of destruction to less enlightened minds!

I found the Lady Chapel a big finely-lighted building with beautifully-decorated walls and fan-vaulted ceiling with more of these delightful painted bosses, for the viewing of which there was a mirror which could be moved on a swivel on the floor in front of the altar. The stone carving around the walls was far beyond my faint power of description. It still had many traces of ancient painting, though many of the statues in the niches were defaced beyond recognition.

Going out of the Cathedral at last, I entered the city with an elevated mind from what I was after seeing in that most enthralling monument from the past. To my surprise too, I found that my headache had gone completely, thank God; and to celebrate that most important event, I went into an eating-house and enjoyed a good meal for the first time since I had arrived in the district. Then I went off to see if I could find anyone who could tell me something more about the wonderful building I had seen.

"What happened to the tower that's missing on the left of the front door of the Cathedral?" I asked a man I saw standing at a corner near the Lamb Hotel.

"I'm blowed if I know, Paddy," he answered. "I don't take much notice of churches. But there was a man over the way that knowed a lot about it some years ago. 'E's dead now, though, so far as I know."

I was glad he answered me at all, after my experience at Witchford, even if he had no information to convey itself.

"Did you ever read anything about it yourself?" I asked.

"Read, is it," he said with a dry laugh. "I can't read. Never went to school, nor never felt the need of it neither."

I walked away to try my luck elsewhere. Seeing a smart-looking young man leaning on a bicycle by the kerb on the opposite side of the street, I went over to him and spoke. He looked startled, as if something unusual had happened.

"Can you tell me anything about the Cathedral, please?" I asked.

"About what?" he said, putting emphasis on the "what" as if he did not fully understand me.

"The Cathedral," I repeated, much louder, in case he was deaf.

"Oh, that old building over there!" he said, as if I had asked about a local gipsy camp. "I knows nothing about things like that. I leaves them to the clergy to look after, and I never goes near them for anything."

With that he pushed his bicycle away, to show me, I thought, that he wanted the conversation ended in the same way as the Witchford people had done.

They don't want to talk to me, I concluded, simply because I'm Irish, I suppose.

Having tried to get into ordinary conversation with two other people, making no mention of the Cathedral at all, I could get no further than a reluctant yes and no to my questions. There was just a vacant look on the faces of those I troubled and I noticed that many of them had very dark brown eyes, a fact I had observed in many of the local people who worked on the aerodrome as well.

Leaving the city, I walked back towards the camp again, wondering at the small minds of people living near a great Cathedral, moreover because I had expected everyone in the County of Cambridge to be highly intellectual on account of having such a world-famous University in their midst.

V   *THE CANTEEN*

It seems that Murthock's final blessing had fallen on me like the sunshine, for my feet were light as I walked along, admiring leaves coming on trees, flowers budding under hedges and green grass covering fields around me, for, thank God, the frost was over. Passing by the aerodrome, I went in to visit the site of the mixer and find out if anyone had taken my place at the cement. I met Cockney Jim on the way with a shovel under his arm.

"Bli' me, Brian, I wish I 'ad your money," he shouted with a broad good-natured smile across his face. "What's up? Havin' a dia off to spend some of it, eh?"

"No, Jim," I answered, noticing that he was covered all over with the grey dust of cement. "I couldn't afford such a thing," and I went on to tell him what was after happening.

"Don't worry," he said cheerfully. "It will all settle itself in time," and he told me of the many similar happenings on the aerodrome since the work started six months before; but unfortunately he talked so quick and used so much slang that I could only catch a word here and there.

"Tell me, Jim," said I, when he had finished, "am I right in thinking the people here don't like the Irish?"

"Bli' me, I don't think they like any outsiders, Brian," said he. "If it goes to that, they dislike the Londoners as much as the Irish, and maybe more, if I know anything."

"What are we after doing to make them feel that way towards us?" I asked, surprised at what he said.

"I'm blowed if I know," said he, with a dry laugh, "but I heeared a bloke sia the other dia that thi've alw'ys been that wia since the time old Hereward the Wike kept their fathers hidin' among the bushes of the fens in olden times."

"But, Jim," said I, "That was a long time ago, wasn't it?"

"It sure was," said he, "but I suppose they have long memories like the Irish!"

Then, with a hearty laugh, Cockney Jim swung the shovel across his shoulder and walked away.

When I reached the mixer I was surprised to find it completely deserted. What must be after happening? I asked myself. Not a single man was near it, so I turned my steps back towards the camp again, passing the works canteen on my way. I heard a voice calling and, looking round, saw the Walking Ganger coming towards me. I expected him to have some bad news, or that he might begin telling me off for breaking up the gang, and causing so much trouble. But instead, he surprised me greatly by talking gently as if nothing in the world had happened between us.

What an amazing man this is! said I to myself.

"Would you like to work in the canteen?" he asked, while a pleasant smile covered his face.

"Of course I would," said I, delighted at the chance of getting away from the shovel and cement.

"Very well then," said he, taking a bunch of keys from the pocket of his long blue flannel coat, picking out two and handing them to me. "These are the keys of the old shack. You can come there to-morrow morning at eight o'clock, start up the fires and boil the water for the men's tea. The cook and her helpers will come there about nine. She will tell you what to do for the rest of the day. One key is for the kitchen; the other for the dining-room."

"The Lord bless you for this," said I, for he was after lifting a great load of trouble from my mind, and I felt extremely grateful. Here was a man with no resentment, I thought; and for the first time in my life I began to see one of the main differences between Englishmen and Irishmen with regard to the harmonious working out of little things that might otherwise lead to any amount of quarrelling.

"Come over now," he said in a kindly way, "and see the cook. You'll find her all right if you do your work."

I followed him along a roughly-paved pathway in an opening cut through a long heap of earth which had been dug out to make way for the foundation of the runway nearby. He introduced me to the cook, Mrs. Long, an Englishwoman, whose husband was a Corkman. She was a big woman with a pleasant face. She told me what I was to do in general as a kitchen porter. Her daughter and another girl helped her, and she said a Dublin man would help me with my work later on. I liked the warm atmosphere of the place. It was really quite comfortable compared with that of the mixer. On my way out I thanked the Walking Foreman again, and then we parted.

I felt the keys in my pocket to make sure of my good luck in case I might be dreaming, and I waved to Cockney Jim as I passed the big mixer where he worked, jingling the keys as I did so, remembering what he had told me about things settling themselves up only a short time before.

If my foot was light coming out of the great Cathedral it was even lighter coming out of the great Aerodrome! I went

38

along like a bird, though I could not help thinking of how sad I had been in the morning at the hateful mixer, and of the long dreary days before, when nobody had time to say a word, not to mind resting, while the big rush was on for the little bonus. That was all over now, thank God. My one-man strike broke up the gang, and strangely enough, there was no punishment following my rebellion. Instead, I had even been rewarded by being given a much lighter and better job at which I hoped to feel content. I found, as I had often done before, that it pays to put up a fight now and again if one wants to get on in life.

That evening when the men returned to the camp from work, one of them, a Dublin man called Tommy Dorman, who lived in the same hut as me, and who was friendly towards me from the start, came along and told me that he had heard about the trouble at the mixer. As a consequence he had put in a good word for me with the Walking Ganger and the canteen staff, all of whom he knew very well, having been with them ever since work on the aerodrome began. So I owed some of my good luck to him. He drove one of the Royal Air Force lorries drawing gravel from the outlying districts and he promised to take me with him to see the country in my spare time later on.

In our hut also was another young man from Dublin, whose foul mouth was a disgrace to that most cultured city, which I never thought could produce a fellow like him. However, I soon found out that many Irishmen took advantage of being in a strange place to show the worst of their character which they would feel ashamed to do at home. Some were married men who thought nothing of going about with Englishwomen while their wives were back at home; a habit which is happily unknown in Ireland, except in very rare cases, because public opinion is so much against it. Englishmen, I was told, act in the same way as soon as they turn their backs on Dover.

Putting the keys of the canteen under my pillow for safety, I noticed for the first time the letters "G.R.," with the impression of a crown on the slip. Examining the rest of the bedclothes, I found the same marks on them.

"The Crown!" I kept saying to myself as I went into bed.

It seemed to recall something to my mind. I wondered what it was, and as I looked again at the covering blanket I remembered. Twelve years previously, while serving in the police at Tallaght, County Dublin, a woman living near the station told my fortune on the cards. I laughed when she told me one thing which I thought would not be likely to happen. "You'll be under the Crown yet!" she said with emphasis. And here I was now, under the Crown on my blanket, and under the Crown in every other respect as well! "What a strange world this is, after all!" said I in my own mind, before going off to sleep.

When I woke in the morning, all was well. The keys were still under my pillow, so it was no dream I had about the canteen! I got out of bed cheerfully, put on my clothes, had a wash and went for breakfast. Then, having returned the mug and cutlery to the hut, I went off in the coach to the aerodrome and, on getting out, went towards the canteen. Everything was quiet there. I put the key in the lock, opened the door of the kitchen and went in.

I cleaned the ranges, put in some papers and dry wood, added coal and put a lighted match to the lot. Both fires lit up cheerfully and I thought that was a good sign. I filled the big urns with water from a tap nearby, put them over the fires and covered them carefully to keep off the soot and dust. While the water was boiling I tidied up the place and swept it out so that in a short time it looked quite neat. The cook had left me some tea, so I pushed one of the urns aside, boiled a small kettle of water in a hurry, made myself a cup, added some sugar sparingly, for it was rationed tightly, stirred it up and enjoyed the drink to perfection.

When the cook and her helpers came we all got busy preparing for the rush of men who were to come into the dining-room for their tea-break at ten o'clock. Shortly before that they began to line up outside the door, but my job was to keep it locked until the proper time so that they would not be annoying the cook beforehand; because people who work outside in this country as well as in Ireland, think that people who work inside have absolutely nothing to do but to dance attendance on themselves.

Just at the stroke of ten she gave me the word that all was

ready, so out I went and opened the door. Once inside, the men lined up in order at the two hatches where the women served the tea which cost a penny a cup. It amazed me how all these fellows had learned to line up of their own accord in so short a time. Some, however, thought only of themselves when they reached the hatches. They came along with pint mugs when the usual ration was only half a pint. An odd rough-spoken Irishman would shout "Full ut up" when the woman had given him more than his right already, after thinking that other men had to be served as well as him with limited tea. However, apart from that, the men's conduct in general was reasonable. They left quietly when they had taken their tea and cheese or margarine sandwiches which were also sold at the hatches. When they were all gone back to work I cleaned the tables and swept the floor. After that I returned to the kitchen to help at washing the ware.

I looked around me as I worked. The building was made of wood and had a corrugated iron roof. There was a homely air about the place and I began to feel happy in it. Washing ware in the sink or putting shovels of coal on the fire now and again was only child's play compared with the hard and hateful job at the mixer. We had our own specially-made cup of what was called "Sergeant Major's tea" also, in the drinking of which the Walking Ganger and other select workers joined us.

When dinner-time came I helped with the big rush of handing out the well-filled plates, mostly of vegetables and a few little bits of meat. After all the men were served I was given my own dinner, and got a very pleasant surprise to find that I had to pay no money for it so long as I was employed in the canteen. That would mean a saving of about thirty shillings a week, so I felt I was really getting on in the world at last after the shaking up I got during the first few weeks.

Time seemed to fly in this job, it was so easy and pleasant. I hardly knew where I was until it was time to go back to the camp. It happened to be pay-day, and as the rest of the staff had left for some time to give a hand at the main canteen at Witchford, I made myself a nice cup of tea after seeing that everything was in order. Then I locked the doors, went across the fields to the pay office, noticing on my way the great and rather sudden bursting out of nature in the shape of lovely rich green shoots of grass, with violets and snowdrops all along the way, except where the great machinery had turned up the soil and laid it in heaps about the place.

Arriving at the office I lined up with the others at the little hatch through which the money was to be handed out as each man gave in his numbered metal tally. In front of me was an intelligent Irishman with whom I got into conversation.

"What do you think of this country?" he asked.

" 'Tis not a bad place at all," said I, "only for the people being so cold and distant compared with the Irish."

"They're like that in a good many places," said he, "but you'll find them a grand people to work with just the same. Give me an English boss any day before an Irishman."

"I'm beginning to learn a little about that myself already," said I, comparing the way the English Foremen had treated me with what I got from some of the lower officers in the Irish police, "and it surprises me greatly as well as making me feel sad."

"I have been around a good deal myself," said he. "I have met the good and the bad, for I spent nine years in America."

"My goodness!" said I in surprise. "Why did you leave it and come over here then?" for I always thought America was the last word in grandeur and abundance, from the looks of those who returned to Ireland from it, and walked about their old familiar haunts as if they actually owned the western continent before coming back to have a look at things at home.

"My dear man," said he with a look of sadness in his eyes, "it is indeed a great country for those who are lucky enough to have employment there, as well as having the sense to mind it. Some of these are among the ones who return to Ireland. But what about the thousands who go to the States and are never heard of again? Drink and starvation is the ruin of some of them. The file of people waiting here reminds me of the bread-lines in New York before the war; but, alas, there were many in America then who had no bread-lines to go to, God help them."

"I had never thought of that, indeed," said I, wondering at my lack of common sense.

"Many more of us never think of it either," said he, "and that is why so many of us are anxious to cross the Atlantic, because we only judge America from the looks of people who come back to show off how well they have got on themselves. We can't see the jobs they have in New York, or the houses they live in either, any more than the Irish at home can see us now, lining up at canteens with our knives and forks, or stuck all day in muddy drains to earn our living."

"How did you get on yourself while you were there?" I asked, thinking that he must be one of the unlucky ones when he left the place and came to work in England instead.

"I was not too badly off at all," he said, "because I had my sister's place to go to when the money ran short. But, God help us," he added with a sorrowful sigh, "no one knows how many people died in the wilds of America in that dreadful time."

"It must have been awful to have been living there then," said I.

"Awful is no name for it, indeed," he said. "Having seen things like that in my time makes me feel quite satisfied in this country, where, if other things are tightly rationed, at least there is plenty of bread for us all, thank God."

I heard a rattle in front of us and, looking up, I saw the hatch opened. As each man handed in his tally he got his pay packet in return. Most of them went off towards the waiting coaches which were to take them to Witchford, but some stood by, looked over the amount recorded on the packets, opened them, took out the money with frowning faces, then stamped their feet on the ground, either because the bonus reward had not come up to their expectations in return for the amount of energy given earning it, or else they thought that too much income tax had been kept from them. They then began to argue with the pay clerk, and he advised them to come back on the following morning when he would explain matters to them. When my turn came to get my packet I secretly thanked the good God that after eleven years of unemployment in Ireland I had at last received an income that might qualify for tax!

I SOON found that nearly all the people of Witchford and Ely were like those to whom I tried to talk and from whom I had got such little response. I wanted to make friends among them but I could not do so. I also found that the Cockneys and the Irish got on very well together. Sometimes the difference in speech made a barrier, but we both laughed over that because we always understood the gist of what was said. Cockneys were accustomed to meeting all sorts of people in London and that made them broadminded, while the people of the Isle of Ely in general are more or less cut off from the rest of the world. Their cold and distant ways gave me a great shock after having left the pleasant friendly people of Kerry such a short time before. I felt lonely and lost in the heart of the vast, flat and uninteresting fens where I now found myself stranded in the needful act of earning my living. In the evening I looked longingly towards the west where the sun was setting, and as I missed the red glow on the skies as well as the deep blue that comes upon the lovely mountains that fringe along the silvery borders of the mighty western sea, I sighed for the happy days gone by for ever. I reflected that if Witchford were an Irish village I would have felt very much at home there from the first evening, and have made a set of friends there as well.

I began to see for the first time that the English and Irish are two distinct races. Never before had that fact become more evident, so I naturally concluded that many of the past troubles between our two countries were as much racial as political.

Another thing that astonished me was that Welshmen working on the aerodrome talked with almost exactly the same brogue as we did in Southern Ireland. On that account many of the English called me "Taffy" because they mistook me for being a Welshman! Up to then I had always thought that Wales was merely an English province like the Eastern Counties in which I was now living. The ways and speech of the Welshmen soon showed me that they were a distinct race from the English. Some of them were fond of telling harmless lies in such a fascinating way that I never lost my temper with them but felt happy being their victim, because of the glaring simplicity of their plots. The Irishman's lie was more subtle; only he could not hide the twinkle in his eye while telling it; and the Englishman's lie was a masterpiece of deceit, because it was accompanied by neither simplicity nor twinkle!

I could not always understand the people from Scotland, but I found them generous, humorous and very like the Irish in their ways. Then it dawned on me that the Welsh, Scots and Irish are all one race; the Celtic; which once owned all these islands before the conquering Romans, Danes and Saxons came with superior numbers and discipline to push them back into the mountains.

With a few exceptions, I had no particularly interesting friends in the camp. They all had different ideas to mine. None of them had the slightest interest in the great Cathedral within such easy reach, nor had they any interest in books. So I felt alone; very much alone.

I wondered where I might be able to find some books, but I had no idea of where to ask about them. I was very anxious to find where Ely was in relation to the rest of England, because I had always thought it was an island somewhere off the coast, on account of it being called "The Isle of Ely." I was therefore astonished and disappointed to find it in the heart of the dreary Fens instead of being out in the open sea with the waves lapping gently round the borders of the abbey lands.

My soul thirsted for knowledge, but I knew there was no chance of getting it at Witchford. So I went off to Ely one day and, looking into a book-shop window I saw a little map of the district on show there. I went in and asked for a copy. The girl behind the counter examined me over and over, as if making a mental note of what I looked like. I took no particular notice of that, however; because so many of the local people had suspicious looks on their faces at the time; so I paid for the map, put it into my pocket and went out. Then I went to a public house next door for a bottle of lemonade. The girl who gave it to me looked friendly, I thought, in contrast to the one who sold me the map, so I casually mentioned the queer looks I was after getting in the book-shop. A thoughtful look came into her eyes at once. Then she too began to look me up and down. Wonderland again! said I to myself. Perhaps she is after all, a sister to the other girl. Maybe they are both the daughters of a pig-buyer who keeps for ever looking over animals with an artful eye for ailments; so I drank my lemonade, wiped my mouth, said good-bye and went out into the street.

Ever since I came to Witchford I had been longing for a chance to visit the town of Cambridge, for my heart was filled with joy at the thought of going into that most famous seat of learning; so the first Sunday that came handy, I dressed up, went to Mass in the Camp Chapel, and then by bus to Ely so as to ask about the best way for getting to the University town. I got off in front of the Cathedral where I was told that a bus would be leaving shortly for Cambridge, so it was with very pleasant hopes I waited for it to arrive at the stop. What a thrill it gave me when at last I saw the big red vehicle come round the corner with the magic name of "Cambridge" printed across the top! I went in, took a seat in the front so that I might see as much of the country as I could on the way, and after all the other passengers had boarded, it moved off.

The journey was not particularly interesting as nobody seemed to bother about talking to another, and the country through which we passed was only a continuation of that about Ely, flat and drab.

At last, however, the spires of Cambridge came into view; then disappeared again because of the woods in between. Meantime we passed by two aerodromes; one at Landbeach; the other at Waterbeach. I was wondering how they got the names with the sea so far away. We passed by a great American camp also and then after a short time we were in Cambridge town, and as the weather had been fine for some time now, everything around looked lovely; trees pushing out their leaves, flowers blooming; lawns and parks looking their best.

When the bus stopped at the end of the journey, I got out and walked towards the first grey building in front of me and, though the back was only turned to me, I guessed that it must be one of the famous university buildings. I was right. It was Christ's College. I went through the little alley that led to the front. Then I turned to the right and walked along until I came to a lovely ancient gateway under an arch in the building. I went in, expecting to find a guide like they have at Glendalough in County Wicklow and other show-places in Ireland. I thought he would be there to tell visitors something about the college, but I was disappointed. There was not even a board put up to tell which of the colleges it was. There was a porter on duty, however, but it seems his work was to look after domestic arrangements for the students entering or leaving the building. He was not a guide. He seemed far more interested in trunks and labels than he was in either history or learning. I ventured in around the place, but not very far, because I was afraid it might be forbidden ground to curious people like me, so I went out through the arch again and crossed the road.

Standing on the opposite side I looked back at the College Entrance. It was a lovely sight. Over the arch was a statue of Lady Margaret Beaufort, who refounded the college at the instance of Saint John Fisher. On either side of that of Lady Margaret were the statues of antelopes, and elsewhere in the design were big roses and other beautiful decorations; the whole lot covered with various coloured paints, now sadly faded after so many years of neglect on account of the war.

I made enquiries for King's College where my friend George Thomson of London had been a fellow some years before. I soon found it. What a thrilling sight it was! I entered the grounds through an ivy-covered gateway in a magnificent stone screen. Before me on the lawn stood a statue of King Henry the Sixth, and to the right was the glorious chapel which he founded. I thought of George Thomson as I went towards it. He went to the Blasket Islands, off the west coast of Kerry, to learn Irish in his youth, and did it so well that he later became a professor of that language and taught Greek and Latin through its medium in Galway University. I had met him in Dublin when he came to help some of my friends to learn the tongue of their own country. I tried to learn it too and failed; but by far the best teacher

I ever met was not one of my own countrymen at all, but George Thomson, the modest young man from London. He told me I had the right brogue for the language but, alas, I was too dull to learn words enough to make that brogue be of any use.

How many a time in the past had I longed for a chance to go to college when I was young in Kerry long ago, and poverty prevented me from doing so! What thoughts came crowding on my soul! Perhaps it was just as well that I did not get the chance, because like a good many others I might not have liked it after all and have made no use of it. Now, however, I was in the grounds of a very famous college. That in itself was a very great satisfaction, for I always loved learning for its own sake; and more perhaps because I could not get it than if I had the chance of doing so.

After feasting my eyes again on the lovely screen, I moved on and entered the magnificent chapel. I was enthralled by its great beauty. Like Ely Cathedral it was full of light, so that I was able to see clearly and admire its soul-stirring features. Tall slender pillars rose from the floor to an immense height from which they branched gracefully upwards and across the roof to meet their equals from the opposite and form the most lovely fan-vaulting I had ever seen. Words fail me to describe this heavenly building. The king who founded it was not a war-monger like those who came before him. He loved learning and religion more than swords and blood. I could not help thinking of that poem of Yeats in which he asks:

> *Where are now the warring kings?*
> *Word be-mockers:*
> *Where are now the warring kings?*

for here was a truly noble monument left by the man of peace, of more lasting glory than any from the men of war.

I came out into the open again with my mind more elevated than it had felt for a long time, thinking of the wonderful skill of the men who had made this most exquisite gem of English architecture in what the present generation is so often pleased to call "the dark ages." It may have been dark in other places, indeed, but certainly not in Cambridge.

I went along to Saint John's College which is entered by another beautiful gateway like that at Christ's. Crossing over The Bridge of Sighs I enjoyed walking about among the cloisters and the woods beyond which had a rich carpet of lovely bright yellow flowers under the trees. It was all like fairyland to me.

I had seen enough of this beautiful and interesting town by now to love the place, though I had barely time to rush about from one building to another. Dear lovely Cambridge! Seat of Learning! Home of Culture! World-famous University! What a stirring place to see!

I walked up and down the streets, meeting some of the students and making it my special business to talk to them. They were extremely courteous. I had no trouble in understanding their speech nor had they in mine. I wondered greatly at this, because most of the English who worked with me on the aerodrome screwed up their faces from the pressure of the riddle in their minds, as if I were a man from Greece who talked to them in Latin! Nor could I understand them either with the terrible monotonous slang they used, even when it consisted only of their very limited stock of words, with the chief emphasis on that filthy imported adjective already mentioned. It seemed so strange to me that the highly cultured students of Cambridge could understand so well an uneducated peasant from the wilds of Kerry, and that he had no trouble either in doing the same with them. I was greatly pleased with my visit, and determined to come back again whenever I grew tired of listening to the crude unvaried language of the building workers.

On my way back to Witchford I looked at the outline of the great Cathedral of Ely, and felt glad that it was from there the idea of the University of Cambridge had first been conceived. Mother and daughter were indeed highly worthy of each other in that case. But how small everything else about that district seemed, compared with the mighty church, and how unworthy the minds of the people in the country surrounding the University too!

THERE was no social life for me at Witchford. Since the locals were so distant towards us we could not go into their houses to talk with them as people do in Ireland, so when I returned from work I either sat on my bed in silence, wrote letters to my friends, or tried to kill time in some other simple way.

Sometimes Michael Darcy and I went out walking and during that time we discussed our various troubles; about our work here, and those concerned with our people in Ireland. Michael was poorly educated, but one of the most generous people I ever met and very nicely mannered as well. I had often heard the others talking with him about the subsistence money to which he was entitled by law for the support of his mother who was a widow in Donegal, but which the overbearing and impudent officials at the Ely Labour Exchange were after refusing to give him. Apparently they saw that he had but little schooling, therefore they thought they had nothing to fear from ignoring his appeals when it saved them the trouble of attending to them. I asked him if it was true, and he said it was; so one evening when we had returned from our walk I felt so annoyed at the glaring wrong being done to him that I asked him would he mind signing a letter if I wrote it to the Chief Labour Exchange in London, because I concluded that such an office should surely exist, in spite of the fact that the Ely officials wanted to give the impression that they were top dogs in the whole organisation. He would certainly be delighted, he said, if I was kind enough to do such a thing; so I sat down, wrote a short note, explaining the situation, as well as giving an account of Michael's circumstances, in the first person, with regard to his widowed mother. Then, after he had signed it, I sealed the envelope, addressed it to:

The Manager of Managers
Head Labour Exchange
LONDON

as I had no means of finding the correct address, went out, and put the letter into the post office. I did not forget to ask the gentleman in London to be kind enough to arrange matters so that Michael might have the money he was entitled to. We both felt that at least we had nothing to lose but the postage, and that we had a few pounds to gain if anything happened in our favour.

Some days later as we walked along the road through the village, we were conversing about the usual things, and had forgotten about the letter, as we watched the various workmen talking in groups, or going into the shops, when a smiling little boy appeared beside us with a sack on his back. I was astonished, indeed, for it was the first friendly smile I had seen on the face of any local person since I had come to the place.

"What have you got in the bag?" I asked him.

"Grass for my rabbits," he said, and then went on in the most friendly manner to tell us all about them.

There was a peculiar charm about this little fellow that was entirely missing from the others I had seen about the place, so I concluded that perhaps he did not belong to Witchford, but was one of the many young people who had been evacuated from the big cities at the time.

"What part of England did you come from?" I asked, holding the sack for him to put in more grass.

"What part did I come from, is it?" he said, laughing, and showing a very nice even set of teeth as he did so. "I was born here."

"Have you lived here ever since?" I asked, still wondering how he managed to be different from the others.

"I have never lived anywhere else only in that Council House over there," said he, pointing to one in a row of houses on our left.

He talked very plain English with a beautiful soft accent and did not use a single word of slang. I could not understand how he managed to do so in spite of the fact that the others around him spoke the language of the working classes.

"What is your name?" I asked.

"Willie Gage," he said.

"A very proper name, indeed," said I, "for you have a most

engaging manner. Have you any trouble in understanding us?"

"Not a bit," he said. "Why should I? You talk English, don't you?"

"Yes," I said, "as near to standard English as Irishmen can get; and, by the way, where do you go for learning?"

"Soham Grammar School," he said, "beyond the city of Ely."

"Do you like it there?" I asked, becoming more interested as the talk went on, and being so glad to find at least one human-minded person in Witchford at last.

"Yes, in a way," he said with a look of sadness in his blue-grey eyes.

"Is there something wrong with it?" I asked, thinking of the master's cane when I was going to school myself.

"Oh, there's nothing wrong with the school," he answered, "but there is a prefect there who tries to make my life a misery whenever he gets the chance."

"That's the way all over the world," said I, remembering the sufferings I went through because of the cruelty of some of the boys in my own time. "Do you like Witchford?"

"I do not," he said, and I could well understand how such a cultured boy should feel unhappy there, because he did not seem to belong to the place at all.

"How old are you, Willie?" asked Michael, who till then had said nothing.

"Thirteen and a half," he said, and he told us so much about himself and Witchford that we got a new interest in the place.

In fact Willie and I became very friendly and had many another talk later on when I met him on his way to the shops and so forth. He was the only steadfast friend I had among the locals and I have kept in touch with him ever since. In the course of our conversation I asked him if he could tell me where I might find books to read, and he very kindly suggested the County Library, in a town called March in the Isle of Ely, to which I might apply for some. It was wonderfully pleasant and refreshing to meet someone so nice in a strange land where the hearts of the people seemed so cold.

Having written so much about the distant ways of the Fen

people in general, I feel like settling matters with my conscience, by saying, as the women of Coomlaegill used to say long ago when criticising their neighbours: " 'Tisn't talking about them I am, why, but alluding!"

We had to wash our underwear in the camp and I always found it a hard job. I never could get shirts to look really clean no matter how I tried. Someone suggested that I should try using soap powder, so I went out to the shop for some.

"May I have a packet of Persil, please?" I asked the woman behind the counter.

She looked puzzled and puckered up her face, so I repeated the name, but there was still no understanding on her part until I pointed to a packet on the shelf behind her. Then she turned about and looked.

"Owah; Poasil," she said, laughing. "You mean Poasil."

"Yes," I said. "I don't care what you call it if it takes the dirt from a grimy shirt."

She handed me the packet and I paid her. Then I went back to the camp wondering which of us had the correct pronunciation!

About a fortnight after meeting Willie I returned from work one evening to find Michael waiting for me with a great light of joy in his eyes. He ran towards me and shook my hand.

"What's up, Michael?" I asked in surprise.

"You got it for me," he said. "You got it."

"Got what?" I asked, not knowing what he meant.

"The money, you devil, you," he said with a broad smile across his face. "The money, man. I got my subsistence allowance," and he danced about the place with joy.

"When did you get it?" I asked, delighted to hear the news.

"When I went to the hut to get my knife and fork at dinner-time I found a letter on my bed. It was a call to the Labour Exchange at Ely, so when I was after my dinner I came back and dressed up before going into the city. Then I went to the works office and told the people there that I was going so that they might put someone else in my place at work."

"I'm glad you did that, Michael," said I. "Decent fellows like you always do. It saves trouble for the ganger."

53

"I suppose it does, indeed," he said, "and mine is one of the best."

"Yes; I remember you telling me that," said I. "But, go on, tell me what happened," I added, suddenly remembering the letter I was after writing to London.

"When I went into the Labour Exchange," said he, "I was taken before a very angry-looking man with a look in his eyes like a hungry hawk going to pounce on a lonely chicken. He was sitting on a tall twisting chair behind the counter like a judge in a court of law, and he gave me hell for leather, right, left and centre with a rasping tongue for daring to write that letter."

"Ah, the blinking old viper," said I in deep derision. "The devil may carry his gab. He thought he could play the game of twisting over the poor ignorant beggars from Ireland as easy as he could swing about in the chair, but we got him from the right quarter where he can't hit back as easily as he hit forward, I'm telling you. Did he find out who wrote the letter?" I asked, fearing that if he knew it I might be getting into trouble later on.

"Good gracious, no, Brian," he said, winking. "He thought I wrote it myself. I only wish I could; but you may be solid sure I paid the piper for it, because he had the value of his money out of me with rotten filthy curses for putting him in so tight a corner for so small a trifle, as he called it."

"Small, is it?" said I, with great disdain on the man of the twisting chair. "Small to him, maybe, but big to people like you and me. What happened next?"

"He gave me a few old papers to sign with a scratchy pen picked up from the counter," he said, "because he would not trust me with the fountain pen he was using himself any more than a jeweller would a blacksmith to fix a clock with a crowbar!"

"That's the way in lots of offices," said I, remembering the same treatment to myself by people who doubted if I could even write at all. "But, go on, tell me the rest," I added, for I was deeply interested in the whole business.

"The angry little terrier finished at last," he said, "by hanging his head in defeat; then counting me out eighteen solid pound notes as back payment for all the time they had

54

done me out of my lawful rights, and telling me that I was to get twenty-eight shillings a week from now on to support my mother!"

"Wisha, may the laurels of glory put rings on your brow, my fine good-natured friend from the Hills of Donegal," said I, shaking his hand and clapping him on the back. "May the world's lasting joy be on you with your great good luck."

"Thank you, Brian," he said, "and I owe it all to you for writing that letter. I could never think of doing it myself. Put that in your pocket now," he added, handing me a lovely new pound note.

I refused to take it, but he forced me so much, saying "You have well deserved it," that in the end I took it to please him. I felt mighty glad and proud that the trifling note I had written for him had found the right man in the right place in London town, and made the wrong man do the right thing in Ely by giving justice and money to Michael in so short a time.

Having written to the Librarian at March on the suggestion of Willie Gage I got a very courteous letter in reply. As I had explained my trouble in getting books, she sent me some, and was also kind enough to invite me to tea with herself and her father on any Sunday I could get to March.

I had bought a second-hand bicycle some weeks before and, being glad at a chance of getting in touch with people connected with books and learning, I cycled to the Librarian's home on the first Sunday I could manage to do so, having previously told her by letter of my intention of visiting her.

When I knocked at the door she received me with the same type of welcome I was used to in Ireland. Miss Phillips was a woman from Scotland who lived in March with her father, a retired Presbyterian clergyman, near the Library. He too gave me a very warm welcome and we had a long and most interesting conversation.

Miss Phillips prepared the tea and put before me such a rich meal as I had not seen since I came to England. Even though everything was tightly rationed on account of the war, she placed two eggs on my plate just as the women of Ireland used to do long ago. I was delighted and extremely thankful because the rationing came very hard on me, having been used to eggs all my life on the farm at home. These two eggs were such a great rarity at that time that I have never since forgotten the person who was kind enough to put them before me. I thoroughly enjoyed the meal as well as the conversation, because we all talked as if we had been old friends.

They laughed when I told them of my surprise at finding the people in the Isle of Ely so poorly educated. Like me, they said, they too had thought, when first they reached the famous Isle, that even plough-boys and milk-maids should all be sort of professors on account of having such a great University near them. How could they avoid learning, they thought, any more than people living near a great brewery could avoid smelling malt! The generosity of these people astonished me. It seemed such a contradiction to the world-wide jokes we all hear about the meanness of the Scots. I said good-bye and came away greatly impressed with the kindness of my new friends and pleased with my visit in general.

There was a fellow by the name of Richard Crowley from Castletown Beare staying in the same hut as me, and when I found where he was after coming from, I asked him if he knew any of my relatives from Annaweelogue.

"Of course, I do," he said. "The two MacFaddens from Dursey Sound near the Yellow Gap are living above here in the Lowlands Camp at Witcham."

"Witcham! Witcham!" I repeated. "It must have been a terrible place for witches around here long ago."

"So it was, indeed," he said. "I'm told there is still a lock on the old font in the Church above there so that witches cannot steal the holy water!"

"The Lord protect us all," said I. "Where is the place?"

"'Tis the next village to this on the road to Sutton and March," he said, "about two miles up the road on your right."

What a strange coincidence, said I in my own mind, that I should now be so near my first cousins in a strange land, having been sent to work in the same district, of all the labour camps in Britain, without any previous knowledge of their whereabouts!

The first chance I got on the following Sunday I cycled to Witcham, having been given the address of my cousins by

Richard and, having talked for a little while with Willie whom I met on the way, I was about a mile beyond Witchford when I saw a blondy-haired young man walking towards me. Something about his appearance told me that he might be one of my cousins whom I had not seen since they were little boys. I got off my bicycle to make sure by asking questions. To my great delight I found I was right in my guess. It was Paddy MacFadden. He was now a fully-grown man, of course. We were both glad to meet each other. He took me back to his own camp at once and introduced me to his brother George and a great many others from Annaweelogue. They all made me feel at home, indeed; giving me what news they could about my relatives and friends beside the western sea. What memories they brought back to me of times gone by!

"Did you know Mike the Joker?" I asked one of them.

"Of course I did," he answered, "but he keeps very much to himself now."

"Does he not go out any more."

"He does not; but he's as lively as ever about the house."

"Wisha, God help him," said I. "That's the way with the world all the time. Why then I remember when he could get about as well as any boy in the place; but age is coming sadly on him I suppose. Does he still live in the little house with the thatch put on right up to the top of the chimney?"

"He does, indeed," said he. Then he paused, smiled and added: "One time when an old beggarman saw the house he thought there was no chimney in it, so he asked Mike how the smoke got out."

"What did Mike say?" I asked.

" 'Och, and sure, that's no trouble at all, my man,' says Mike, says he. 'We take it out in bags!' "

I asked how long they had been at work in Witcham and they said about six months; ever since the aerodrome started at Sutton.

"But some of us will never leave the place by the look of things," said Denisheen Denny Den with a knowing look and a wink over the shoulder of my cousin George.

"How is that, eroo?" said I.

"There is a nice young girl by the name of Doris Wyand-ham living up at Sutton and I'm afraid she gets more

57

attention from George than either his mother or his work does these days."

"None of your old guff now," said George with a good-humoured smile. "You have me shamed all over the country since I came here. Go home yourself and marry Nell the Herrings with a face on her like the Queen of Sheeba, for no one else can keep you in your place."

"Who is Nell the Herrings?" I asked.

"Yerra, blast her," said my cousin Paddy, "she's a leeching old tripe that goes around the town selling fish whenever there's a fair in Castletown Beare."

They went on like that with pleasant banter while my cousins prepared a meal for me on the camp stove.

I felt very happy that night as I returned to Witchford, and I thanked God for having sent me to where my own relations were living, even if the district in general was so very in-hospitable itself.

Some weeks afterwards I was introduced to Doris Wyand-ham who was later on to become the wife of my cousin George. She was a nice girl with dark curly hair and a cheer-ful ringing laugh, which was so refreshing in this, the land of lonesome faces!

VIII *THE KING'S SCHOOL*

ONE Sunday evening I went to Ely for a further look around the Cathedral because I never grew tired of its magnificence. In my wanderings I came to a big block of ancient buildings under which a great archway called Ely Porta was built. This was formerly the main entrance to the monastery. On either side of it on the inside were doors leading to a tower over-head, and as I was anxious to find out all I could about such an interesting place, and had no one to show me about, I became determined to find out for myself, so, seeing one of the doors open, I ventured in. It led to a stone stairway which I had no hesitation in ascending. At the top I found another doorway which led into a schoolroom. As there was nobody about I glanced at some of the books, envious of those who had them while I had none. In one desk I picked up a copy of *The Pilgrim's Progress*, which I had already read in Ireland. It had nice coloured pictures, and as this was the Bunyan country I was doubly interested in reading it again, moreover the introduction, which gave an account of the life of the famous tinker. I noticed that the name of the owner was Graham Hodges. I wished I could get to know him so that I might ask him to lend it to me, but as I had no means of doing so, I put the book back, and went towards a raised platform at the end of the room where I saw a piano standing. Going up to it I sat on the stool and started to play with one hand "The Wearing of the Green" as a sort of musical protest against the strange ways of the Fenland people! There was quite a temper rising within me like a French Revolutionary playing the Marseillaise, when the sound of footsteps on the boards behind me brought me to my senses and I realised I was a trespasser. I looked around and saw a tall young man of about nineteen standing in the doorway; but before I had time to explain my business he had turned away and gone down the stairs again. I thought he might be going for a policeman or something like that, so I hurried out of the room and down the stairs after him. There he was, standing at the bottom, waiting for me. I explained my position in a few words. He listened with the greatest courtesy, and as the conversation went on, I found that he was a prefect of The King's School attached to the Cathedral. He was a highly-cultured intelligent boy. He told me all he could about the school and Ely in general, which none of my companions on the aerodrome could do. When I told him I thought he intended to report my presence as an intruder in the building, he laughed and said he had no such intention, as he was quite used to seeing people anxious to learn all they could about such an interesting collection of buildings as Ely could boast of to the world.

For some time I had been wondering if my opinion of the local people was not in some way prejudiced, or that perhaps my imagination had gone wrong owing to the change of air or some other unaccountable cause, so I decided on asking this young man a question on the subject, after he had told me he was not a native, but had come from Northampton.

"I have formed a certain opinion about the people of this district," said I, "and before telling you what that opinion is, I would like to hear what your own is first, so that I may be better able to judge whether I am right or wrong in mine."

"The people about here?" he asked.

"Yes," I said. "The ordinary people living in the Isle of Ely."

He rubbed his hand over his face for a minute as if in deep thought, pursing his lips as he did so.

"Well," he said slowly and with deep emphasis, "in the first place they're not generous."

"To my great disappointment I have found the same thing about them since I came here," said I; glad to find that at least in one respect my imagination was not running away with me. "Whatever other faults the Irish have," I added, with a certain amount of justified pride, "that is not one of them."

"I don't know many of your people," he said, "but the Yanks told me the Irish are very good-natured."

"The same can be said of the Yanks themselves," said I, feeling proud also of the Stars and Stripes and of Ireland's great connection with America. "But go on, please tell me more about the people here."

"In the second place," he said, "they are very poorly educated, though we can blame them less for that than for lack of generosity, because it is only quite recently they began to go to school at all."

I was amazed to hear this. I thought that even if they ignored the University itself, they might at least have been interested in ordinary schools. I had been asking myself too if these people were typical of the race which had ruled three-quarters of the world for centuries, and if so, how did they manage to do it? They had at least succeeded in making a rebel of me in any case, and I kept asking myself if such a race was really fit to rule anyone, and that if ever they went back to rule Ireland again I should be first in the ranks trying to get them out. The young man saw the look of surprise in

my face as my eyebrows wrinkled in a puzzled gesture at what
he was after telling me, so he continued:

"They never bother their heads about learning," he said.
"Their whole outlook is attending to pigs and cattle so that
they may get every penny they can from the lands they own."

"Farmers are the same where I come from," said I, "but at
least they have a lot of natural wit and humour so that the
most ignorant among them would seem an educated man
compared with the people here. I think mountainy men are
always like that, in spite of the fact that they have no chance
of being shown the way to better things."

"Learning, is it?" he said with a laugh. "Even the common
people living in the town of Cambridge itself dislike the
University which is to the outside world its principal glory.
In the past there was many a fight between what they call
'Town and Gown.' "

"For pity's sake! I thought we had queer ways in Ireland,"
said I with a smile, "but I'm afraid you English have beaten
us in that respect after all. Man alive, sure we live for ever
thinking of the glories of our early Christian Universities,
Glendalough and Clonmacnoise, where only the round
towers, storied ruins and lonely tombstones remind us that
they ever existed, so I'm damned sure we should think it a
great honour if we could boast of such a lovely living place
as Cambridge is to-day."

"The intellectual English see things that way," he said,
"but the working classes would rather see the colleges cleared
away with bull-dozers so that they might get jobs and earn
bonus putting up offices in the shape of great concrete boxes
in their places."

Then I remembered the remark of a woman living in the
town who said she hated the sight of the colleges because
they looked so much like prisons. Neither she nor her family
had the slightest interest in Cambridge as a University Town.
They were all very well mannered in spite of that, but I was
greatly surprised to learn that they thought it no honour to
be living in such an interesting place. No, their thoughts
were in the opposite direction. They had no hankering after
learning or books like I had. Their chief ambition was to

start a pig farm right beside the great academic buildings and among the mortar boards of Cambridge!

"I only wish I could meet more people like you," I said, "who could tell me something about the place in the very intelligent way that you have done, and I would like to come back here some time later on to find out more about your school."

"I'm sure the Head Master would like to meet you too," he said, "because he is very kind and courteous to anyone in search of learning, let him be young or old."

"I am very glad to hear that," said I, "and I intend to come along as soon as ever I get the chance."

We parted then and I was very pleased to have met at least one intelligent person in the district. I was also glad to find that my mind was not exactly so deranged as I feared it might have been, because here was a young man who saw things in the same light as I did, although we were strangers in almost every other respect.

In the course of a few days I returned to the school to see the Head Master. When I opened the door of the same room I was surprised to find it full of boys, and a master standing on the platform in front of them. I felt like being back in school again as I moved towards the master to explain my visit, and as I did so I was surprised when all the boys stood up suddenly as a mark of respect, without being told to do so. I was pleased and flattered by this show of honour for a mere Irish peasant, so I looked at the boys, smiled and nodded to them to sit down again. Then, with a certain amount of embarrassment, I frankly told the master who I was, and confessed that I had been in the school before and looked over some of the books. His face flushed, but more I thought from shyness than anger as he gently reprimanded me by saying: "You must not investigate in the school."

"I had no intention of doing anything wrong, Sir," said I, realising that I was a trespasser in a world to which my kind did not belong, like the little man who followed his cow into the fairy mansion at Coomlaegill long ago, so I explained about my frantic search for books, and asked if I might see the Head Master.

"I am the Head Master," he said, as another boyish flush

came over his gentle-looking features, "and it is my duty to keep things in order here. However," he added, "I'll see if I can help you with books later on if you get in touch with me, but in the meantime I must attend to the class."

When he conveyed me to the door as a gesture of courtesy I felt that I was after meeting a young man of great politeness and that the whole atmosphere of the school was that of most unusual refinement. I began to feel that it was no place at all for a peasant to visit, in spite of the fact that I was greatly impressed by what I had seen and heard.

"Go back to the canteen where you belong," I heard a voice saying inside me as I went down the stairs, "and leave the books and learning to your betters. The spade will always get you bigger money than the pen."

"But I can't use a spade," I argued with myself, remembering how often I had tried and failed for lack of strength and interest in the job of turning up the ground.

"Well then, you must be content to stay for ever poor," I said, as I took the road back to Witchford, turned into the hut and sat on my bed to finish off my thinking.

I could not rest, so I took up my pen and wrote a letter to the Head Master, apologising for going into the school without an introduction, and trying to get further information about my difficulties. Then, after going out to post it, I returned and went to bed.

In the course of a few days I had a nice letter from him inviting me to his place of lodging for a talk after school hours. I went to see him at the appointed time, of course, and he received me with a courtesy and kindness that was really refreshing. He had the same gentle modest manner as George Thomson of whom he reminded me very much. We talked of many things, but mostly about books in which he too was greatly interested. I asked him if he could manage to lend me *The Pilgrim's Progress* which I had previously seen in the school. He went out of the room, brought back the owner, Graham Hodges, and asked him if he were willing to lend it to me. He said he was, of course. He was a nice quiet boy from London and his father had sent him to Ely because he wanted him educated beside the great Cathedral so that it might help to elevate his mind, as I know it did. He went out for the book, returned with it and handed it to me. I thanked him and then he went away after saying good-night to both of us. This greatly surprised me, for we never say good-night in Ireland before the fall of darkness. He seemed completely at home in the Master's presence. I thought of how different matters were with me long ago, for I was still somewhat afraid of my old Head Master up to the day he died, although I was thirty years old at the time!

When I mentioned the coldness of the local people, he took their part, for he was a man with no inclination to speak badly of anyone.

"They are not a demonstrative people," he said, "but they're as good as gold when you get to know them."

Before I left that evening a lot more of the boys came to say good-night to him, so that I was greatly impressed by the feeling of mutual respect in the place. He explained that the school specialised in that particular kind of courtesy. He treated me to tea, and as the conversation went on I knew I had met a most interesting man. Then when I said good-bye and left for Witchford, I felt that there were still many excellent people in England, even if they seemed as scarce as precious diamonds among the drab and dreary Fens.

IX   *A SPY FOR GERMANY*

I HAD been working happily in the canteen for some weeks now and had almost forgotten my trouble at the mixer when the young Corkman who had advised me about the danger of dermatitis from the cement came to talk with me at the hatch one day as the others sat at their dinner. I thanked him for his advice as I had not seen him for some time.

"Oh, don't mention it, indeed," he said. "I knew from the start that you were not the man for the mixer, and I like to put a fellow on the right track if I can do it."

"I always find the County Cork fellows decent like you," I said, remembering the great kindness the people of Kilmurray in that County had shown me when I had gone there some years previously to search for possible relatives of mine; and the fact that Moya Llewelyn Davies who used to shelter Michael Collins during the Anglo-Irish war had told me that he was the very soul of generosity.

"A word of help costs nothing," he said. "But, listen here a minute: do you see your old ganger over there in the corner?" he added, looking cautiously over his shoulder at Angus O'Donnell, who had his back to us as he talked with his companions.

"Yes," I said. "I see him and I don't think he is a very bad fellow after all, only for being so terrible ignorant."

"That's the trouble with a lot of people in the building trade," he said. "Not alone are they ignorant but what is worse, like a pack of puny pishkins, they don't want to learn."

"Well, I suppose it takes all kinds to make a world," said I, "as the old saying goes, but learning is no load to anyone."

"That's true for you, indeed," said he, bursting suddenly into laughter.

"What are you laughing at?" I asked, looking behind me in case someone was about to play a trick on me.

"I'm laughing at what your old ganger said the other day," said he, "when he saw you in here."

"What did he say?" I asked, full of eagerness to find out what was thought of me after breaking up a gang, and feeling that it would not be very complimentary.

"He looked at you," said he, "when he saw you smiling all over the place, 'hail fellow well met' with everyone in the canteen, and says he: 'Look at him in there now,' says he. 'Look at him. That man broke my heart!'"

"The devil mend it for him then," said I, "for I didn't mean to hurt him, but I made solid sure that he was not going to break mine if I could help it."

"The blessing of God on you for it," said he, going back to his seat at the table.

The world was full of new hopes for me now, thank God. The air was kind, for the frost and fog had gone completely. Every day was crisp and sunny, but in spite of it all, things were not going too smoothly in the canteen. There was a local girl employed there who did not worry much about work while I did the surplus in case of need. Now and again when I thought I had my fair share done and left the excess, the cook began to call my attention to it. When this went a bit too far I answered back with all the vigour of a pent-up Irish temper. She had no liking for that at all, but I had no honey to coat my language with. Now and again she ordered my friends out of the kitchen as well, though it was very seldom they troubled her, indeed. In a few words, relations were strained in the place for, like love, the course of cooking has its harrowing seasons too. Then one day some of her own friends who were in a position to supply her with "fully-fashioned" stockings, came into the kitchen, and I, in a most uncharitable manner, ordered them out in the same way as she had done to those who came to see me. They went out peacefully enough, for I had nothing against them nor they against me, and I had only done it to show the cook that I could be awkward too. One of the men was Mackey Williams, a dark-haired, rather yellow-faced Englishman I had known for some time, and about whom I had no complaints, but whom I had reason to remember later on.

During my dinner hour each day I liked to read a little of what I could lay hands on, never minding who was looking at me, and wholly forgetting that reading of any sort is looked at with suspicion by most of the working classes. Sometimes I opened up the little map I was after buying at Ely and studied my position in the Fens; now and again asking questions about the different villages around the place for the mere pleasure of getting information and filling up the blankness of my mind. But one day as I was washing ware at the sink I felt a tap on my shoulder from behind. Looking back I was amazed to find the General Foreman right beside me. I was greatly startled because he was a very distant man in his ways and even colder-looking than any of the Fenman, though in fairness to him I must say that any request I had ever made to him was granted at once. He had replaced the curly-headed General about six weeks previously.

"Let me see that map you've got," he said.

66

"Certainly, Sir," said I, going to my jacket and taking it from the pocket, wondering at the same time how in the name of goodness he found out that I had it.

He took it from me and walked out of the kitchen without another word, for silence seemed for ever golden in the hollow of his heart. I thought perhaps he wanted to locate some particular place in it and I felt rather honoured at the idea of such an important man coming to borrow an Irishman's map when he could easily get one of his own. I knew it would be quite safe anyhow and would not go astray, because I had written my name on the front of it.

Things went on normally in the canteen after this, in spite of the little bickerings which are usual in every walk of life. I had forgotten all about the map until a few evenings later as I was sitting on my bed in the hut, because of lack of chairs, I heard a knock at the door. One of the men went to see who was there and I heard someone asking for me by name. Before I knew where I was two well-dressed men came up to me. I wondered who the blazes they were, for I had never seen them before. They soon told me, however; two plain-clothes policemen from the town of March who had come to question me. When I asked to see their identity cards they showed them to me at once. "Go ahead then," I said. "Ask any questions you like," for it seemed to me that though Hereward was dead, the Fens were awake at last! They were very polite about it all. They had come, they said, because of a complaint made by a girl from an Ely public house that a stranger told her he had bought a map. She thought it very unusual for a common labourer to do so, except for some unlawful purpose, moreover as he sounded like an Irishman; it being well known that Ireland wanted to stay friends with Germany; the Irish Government having declared its intention of staying out of a war beyond its pale. That was of course as much as to say "Hail Hitler!" in the eyes of thoughtless English people who expected everyone to be on the side of their country. I had been reported also by a customer at the canteen, said the detectives, because he saw me poring over the map and thought it his duty to his country to have the matter looked into on account of the dangerous times we were living in. So there was nothing for me but to prove my innocence by telling them why I had it and letting them see the contents of my cases as well. I told them frankly why I had the map; explaining that they were for sale to the public and that I could not see anything wrong in buying one; certainly not to light my pipe with, but to use it in the way all maps were used since Noah came out of the Ark. Then, as I opened my cases I caught a twinkle in the eye of one of the police. "That's all I have in your country," I said; "a little less than the tinkers have in my own," and then I saw two twinkles instead of one. They looked over what I had in the cases, put everything carefully back when they were finished, said good-bye and went their way.

I thought I might never see the map again except in a court of law. Yet, as I knew I had a clear conscience I felt that everything would turn out all right in the end. Still, on second thoughts, I could never know. It was a time of awful and terrible war, and I had read somewhere about an innocent Frenchman who was executed during the Revolution; his only crime being that he had been found with a book in his pocket! It would not surprise me at all if the ignorant people among whom I was then living would not easily extend their witch-hunts to include maps as well as books.

Everyone about the place at that time seemed extremely patriotic, with a man called Winston Churchill as their principal hero. Churchill was right in this; Churchill was right in that; and in the presence of the labouring classes the man who said anything against him had great courage indeed. If the sun shone, Churchill was praised; if the clouds came down, Hitler was blamed! I knew nothing of Churchill, so I could not say either yes or no about him, but when some of the English labourers talked about the meanness of the Irish in keeping out of the war, I told them at once that they had every right to do as they pleased, because they had fought for seven hundred and fifty years for such a right, and good luck to them with it.

"But, Pat," said one of them, "it's your war as well as ours. You know as well as we do that the Germans are no use. I can't see for the life of me why you Irish are so much in favour of them. Bli' me, you mustn't be in your right senses."

" 'Tis hard to know what sense is these days, indeed," said

68

I, "and it can't be a crime for us to do as we choose, and stay away in quietness from the scene of other people's battles."

"Bli' me, Pat," he said, "you have it all wrong. I never knowed an Irishman to see things in a proper way. What makes you want so much to like the Germans?"

"They never did us any harm since Adam was a boy," said I, "and in the past I know 'tis true your people liked them greatly if the history books have truth said on their pages."

"I don't know what you're talking about, Pat," said he.

"It is not so very long ago at all," said I, "since the Queen of this country married a German Prince, is it not?"

"I don't know nothin' about that," said he, " 'cause I don't read 'istory."

"If you did," said I, "you would know that the people of this land were madly in love with the Germans in the past. They paid German soldiers, called 'The Hessians,' to crush the Irish rebels in 1798 when decent elements of the British Army didn't want to do it, and if we go back a little further we find the English in the eighteenth century preferring a German to rule over them instead of a Briton."

"You must be rambling, Paddy," said he. "I know lots of things but I never heard that before. When all is said and done, you know as well as I do that Britannia rules the waves, not to mind the country. Who was this German you're ravin' about?"

"Raving, is it?" I said. "I'm not raving but stating facts. Loyalty to royalty is an obsession with the English, but in this case their choice was not British at all."

"Who was he then?" said he. "Come on, tell us."

"The Germans called him 'George of Hanover,'" I said, "and the English called him 'George the First.'"

"Well, I'm blowed!" said he. "Where did you read about that?"

"In a very well-written history of your country by a man called Arnold-Forster," I said. "And furthermore, there is one special chapter in it that you should read carefully."

"What one is that?"

"The one headed: 'Our German Forefathers.'"

"Go on, Paddy," said he with a laugh. "I don't believe that."

"Nor do I neither," said one of his companions.

"Well then," said I, "all you have got to do is to get the book and see for yourselves."

"Book, is it, Paddy!" said he. "We couldn't be bothered readin'. We sees enough o' the Germans without readin' anythin' more about them."

Seeing that I could get nowhere with them as far as history went I gave up the argument; the only thing I was forced to accept from them being the title of "Paddy," though I told them that it cost my people money to call me Brian! The English, however, persisted in calling every Irishman "Paddy" for nothing. In spite of that, in all fairness, I must add that I could always argue with the majority of Englishmen without having the slightest fear of having my head broken on the way home as might have happened to one of them if he argued with half the heat against the Irish.

A few days after the March detectives' visit I was searching for something in one of my suitcases when I suddenly came across the map I had seen in their hands. How in the name of goodness did it come to be here again? I asked myself. Then a thought struck me. They were satisfied that I had no bad intentions, and had slipped the map into the case while I was not looking. Good fellows, indeed, said I in my own mind, for then I knew the trouble was ended.

I also found out who it was that saw me with the map in the canteen, and reported me. It was Mackey Williams, the young man I had ordered out of the kitchen. He came up and confessed it to me, and my admiration for his frankness in telling me killed any smouldering resentment I might otherwise have for him over it, even though, under the circumstances, his motives did not appear to be altogether patriotic.

TIME was rolling on nicely for me, with sunshine every day outside and pleasant work within. I had been in the canteen for a few months now, and was quite happy there. I was kept busy each day till dinner-time, attending to fires, washing ware and helping to take drums of tea to the waiting lorries so that they might be driven along to the different gangs; but when dinner was over I had an easy time. There was always plenty to do, of course, but no rush.

As everything good comes to an end, however, my job in the canteen was no exception. The domestic side of the business was not exactly as pleasant as it had been at first, so that I felt glad in a way, when a secret message came to me from a Corkman by the name of Charley Desmond who was a clerk in the General Foreman's office, asking if I would be willing to take his place while he was on holiday in Ireland. I was glad of a chance to try my hand at office work, for I thought it would be nice to be wearing clean clothes all day instead of dirty overalls; and of course I concluded that my canteen job would be waiting for me when I came back. So I took a run across the fields to see Charley.

"What made you think of me for the job beyond all the others?" I asked when we were alone in the office, for I felt I had been honoured by the invitation instead of being degraded to the pick and shovel as might have happened.

"Well," he whispered, putting his fingers to his lips to denote secrecy, because of the thin partition between us and the next office, "the fact of the matter is that about a week ago the General Foreman asked me if I knew anyone among the workers who might be handy with the pen, and I suggested you."

"But why me?" I persisted, wondering how he found out that I could write at all.

"The General took a map from you some time ago and left it here in the office," said he. "Your name was written on the front of it, and when I pointed it out to him as evidence of your hand-writing, he agreed to give you the job."

"The Lord be praised for turning evil things to good," said I with joy in my heart. "Promotion to the canteen came because a ganger reported me to the firm; now, by God's grace, promotion is after coming again because someone reported me to the police!"

"'Tis all with God, indeed," said Charley, "glory be to His Holy Name. You never know what luck there is before you in such a world as this."

"That's true for you, indeed," said I. "Good things are always but a house-and-a-half away, if we could only pass the corner and find their hiding-place. At home in Ireland where the work is scanty we must coax the powerful if we want position; a roll of butter for the local doctor or a laying pullet for the parish priest may work a wonder that may put a beggar on the pathway to success."

"You're after saying a mouthful there," said Charley. "There's no need now for presents to get jobs in England."

"The English are the pets of God in many ways," I said, "though they often have to pay for it in wars and other troubles that the Irish never know. But, anyhow, when do you want me to start here?"

"You can come to-morrow if you like," said he, "and before I go I'll show you what to do till you get the run of things."

"The Lord keep safety on your journey," said I, "and thank you very much."

"Oh, don't mention it indeed," said he. "You're doing me a favour, for I'm going across the sea on Sunday, so you can take my place the following morning. I'll tell the General about it when he comes in."

Going back to the canteen I looked around me at the place where I had spent so many happy days, and felt really lonely to be leaving it. I consoled myself, however, that I would be coming back again, and, anyhow, I felt I was going up in the building world, like Tim Finnegan carrying the hod! The sun was shining brightly every day so I had nothing to worry about except that I was a very poor hand at figures. That, I knew, would be a hell of a draw-back in an office. I was still very green about conditions in the building trade and its very shaky type of security, but I was always ready to learn wherever I went.

The following day I started in the office, dressed in my suit of Irish tweed from the Mills of Murt O'Shea at Ashgrove near Kenmare. Charley trained me in to the run of things from that till the end of the week, so that when Monday came I was feeling fairly self-possessed at the job. There was another clerk, a Londoner, with me, and he was kind enough to help me when I got into difficulties, which was fairly often. The General only called in now and again as he was kept busy going around the site all day in his van instructing the gangers about their work. During his brief visits to the office he stayed very quiet, and though he never troubled us in any way, his presence had a freezing effect on everyone so that we all felt glad when he went off again.

Though I was now dressed up like others in the offices I did not feel as happy as I thought I would, because the dry figures annoyed me and I was far too slow in dealing with them. Our tea was made by a little boy from London, whose people sent him on to Ely from the danger of the bombs, but he was such a poor hand at either making fire or tea that I took over the job from him now and again as a sort of merciful relief from all the cursed figures.

I always thought office people were highly paid, but got a shock when pay-day came to find I only got the same wages as I had for work in the canteen. I learned another thing too; that an office job was by no means the sunshine it had seemed before I went to work at it myself. God help us, I spent half my time trying to keep awake as well as doing the figure work, sitting lazily at the desk. Sometimes I took in the men's checks after they had finished work and had many dealings with the gangers as well. It was amazing how polite they all got to me, especially Angus O'Donnell from fair Donegal, whose gang I was after breaking up! In spite of that, however, I found the job was no promotion as far as money went, but on the contrary, because I had now to pay for my dinner instead of having it free as I had while working in the canteen.

When the month was up I was glad to see Charley come in the office again; but I got a shock when the General told me to report to a ganger on the site instead of going back to the canteen where I was needed no longer. My spirit seemed to sink to my toes, but I had to accept the decree of fate, as there was nothing I could do to stop it.

From that day forth my star of good luck began to set slowly and surely; but as the sun was still shining brightly I did not notice it so much at the time. Beginning a new job, however, I felt greatly humiliated at having to get back into overalls again. I felt degraded, but I was lucky to find a nice English ganger to rule over me. The job we had to do was very monotonous; brushing loose gravel and rubbish from the newly-made runways, from morning to evening, day after day. The weather was very hot, too, and if it had not been for the good luck of having Murthock in the gang to cheer me up with his witty sayings, the time would have seemed much longer.

"Have you any notion of going back to Ireland, Murthock?" I asked, as we brushed along together.

"Sorro' the hate then, indeed," said he, wiping the sweat from his brow, "while I'm earning big money in a lovely job like this forninst the door of my little hut. Big Paddy over there is just after coming back. He'll tell you all about the old country," and he pointed across the runway to another jolly Irishman called Joyce from Connemara.

"What was it like in Ireland, Paddy, when you were home?" I shouted across to him.

"Fair enough, you know," said Paddy, leaning on his brush. "As long as they have the spuds and turf for the winter they don't care a devil about anything else out there except an odd time when a hungry sow comes along and starts eating the bottom of the half-door!"

"What ate the other half of it?" asked Murthock with his usual sharpness.

"There never was another half," said Paddy. "By the hoakey-poakey, man, they couldn't afford it!"

"Did you find your people all right?" asked Murthock.

"Oh, fit as a fiddle, indeed," said Paddy with a broad smile. "The place we live in is very wild, you know, as you may have guessed from seeing myself that's like a scarecrow in a garden when the blossoms do be coming on the spuds."

"I don't think you are the worst of them either," said I, remembering the other Connemara man that came across with us in the boat wearing an old coat the colour of the covering on a bog that's burnt from the sun.

"Wisha, God help us," said he, "I suppose I'm no better than the rest of them, for the little house we live in is so low that you could pat it on the back like a dog!"

"What name do you call it then?" I asked, laughing at the description.

"Upon my honour then," said he, "we weren't short of names for it at all, though we might be short of other things. 'Smoky' we called it, man. 'Smoky' is the name, and smoky it is, as sure as there's a cross on an ass. 'Tis many an evening after sitting on the ditches listening to the gowereen rue that I went in and saw my mother in the corner like a blinking kippered herring!"

"What is the gowereen rue?" asked Murthock, who came from a part of Ireland where there is little Irish spoken.

"The Jack-snipe," said Paddy, "that makes a sound at nightfall in the lonesome boglands for all the world like the bleating of a goat."

The Walking Ganger who had given me the job in the canteen had left and there was a new man in his place; a very fat red-faced little fellow from Yorkshire. He was quite decent, but like all men of his class, we liked him better when he was away than when he came to see us. Paddy, who could talk Gaelic, called him "The Puthoageen Yarg," which meant "The Little Red Pudding," but Murthock soon changed that to "The Yorkshire Pudding" which is a name the English have for a sort of Jack pancake with no sugar in it, served with hot meat dinners.

As time went on, the job got more lonely, and there were still miles of runways to be swept, so when we reached a spot near a wood at the top of the aerodrome we took it by turns to go into a meadow among the trees for a rest, and to get away from the glaring sun for a little while. One day, however, when my turn came, I lay on the grass and fell asleep; then woke up suddenly thinking that I had slept much longer than I actually did. I hurried back to my place with the brush; full of excitement and wanting to make up for lost time by sweeping with a lot of new vigour.

"The God of Mankind be praised," said Murthock, "that rest did you good, by the way the life is after coming back into you. I own to the devil, if the firm had only sense enough to send us all into that meadow we might earn a lot more bonus than we are from leaning on the handles of the brushes till the shadow of the ganger makes us move along a bit."

"Was he here while I was away?" I asked; a guilty conscience for a comrade putting fear into my heart.

"He was indeed," said Murthock; a look of great concern coming into his eyes.

"Bad manners to him, what did he say?" I asked, in great anxiety, for I expected to be reported as being missing from the job.

"You were listening to what he said, weren't you?" said Murthock, turning to Paddy who was in the act of filling his pipe.

Paddy just nodded, and I thought I could see the glint of a small twinkle in the corner of his eye as he held on to the pipe he had between his broken yellow teeth which were showing as the ghost of a half-doubtful smile was stealing over his naturally jovial features. I thought it rather mean of him to even feel inclined to laugh at me for being in trouble, not to mind doing so in a big burst as many would have done, but I kept my mind to myself for the time being.

"What did he say, is it?" Murthock went on. "What didn't he say? you should have asked. Welcome be the will of God, man, he finished up in the end by saying you weren't fit to be boiled for dogs!"

"What did you say when you heard that?" I asked, highly indignant at the ganger for saying such a nasty thing about me.

"I told him you were!" said Murthock, moving away from the reach of my brush, and bursting into a hearty laugh.

"The devil may carry your gab," said I, greatly relieved as I joined in the laugh.

Cockney Jim and other Englishmen worked with us, and they were as tired of the job as we were, but consoled themselves that at least it was better than being in German concentration camps or other horrible places which the curse of war had struck. When news came that one of their friends was killed they simply said: "Old Sam's gone over the top." That was all; and they went on with their work as if old Sam had never existed. The word "old" did not mean either age or wrinkles, for "old Sam" might be only half the age of the man who mentioned his death. But before I found this out, when I heard them referring to myself as "old Brian" I was troubled, for I thought age had suddenly caught up with me before my time! The man who was killed had his whole history, monument and memory enshrined in these simple words: "Old Sam's gone over the top!" He was after dying for his country, I thought, and surely he deserved at least a few words more, even if he did not get the dampness of a welling tear. If he had been an Irishman dying for Ireland we would never hear the last of him in songs and lamentations. Even his thirty-first cousins, lucky enough to survive, would live for ever after in the limelight of his glory, and expect to share the honour with him, even if there was nothing whatsoever earning honour in themselves.

I think that is the attitude to life and death which gives the English power to beat us always in commercial competition. When a house is bombed and a family killed, they begin at once to clear away the debris and build another and a better house in its place. But in Ireland, alas, we are inclined to leave the debris as it is and get upon our knees to curse the people causing it for seven generations! Then we start to form committees to make collections for a noble monument to keep the memory of the dead for ever green.

We had many friendly arguments with the English about these things; the English praising Churchill and the other leaders of the day, and making little mention of the heroes of the past. As Irishmen, of course, we went much further back in history for the people that put lustre on our land.

Murthock had a nice voice and raised it sometimes:

> *We are the boys of Wexford*
> *Who fought with heart and hand,*
> *To burst in twain the galling chain,*
> *And free our native land.*

77

After him, but in much rougher tones, Paddy would follow:

> When all beside a vigil keep,
> The West's asleep; the West's asleep:
> Alas, and well may Erin weep
> When Connaught lies in slumbers deep. . . .

"Bli' me, that's the way you should be too," interrupts Cockney Jim with a touch of good-humoured sarcasm.

"The devil's cure to him," said Murthock, "if he was lying in that meadow above it would help the war effort as much as having him here."

Then suddenly Paddy raises his voice and starts to brush very briskly as he sings loudly:

> But, hark, a voice like thunder spake,
> The West's awake! The West's awake!
> Sing, oh, they died their land to save,
> On Aughrim's slopes and Shannon's waves!

finishing with a hearty laugh in which we all join.

Leinster and Connaught had done their part, so, being a Munsterman I did not want to let it go with them, and chanted like a croaking raven:

> Oh, Limerick is beautiful as everybody knows,
> And by that city of my heart, how proud old Shannon flows;
> It sweeps down by that dear old town as pure in depth and tone
> As when Sarsfield swept the Saxons from the Walls of Garryowen.

Then I too swept my brush with vigour across the runway to show how the job was done, though I couldn't help thinking how strange it was that so many "sons of the Gael" and "men of the Pale" should now be earning their living side by side with the same Saxons we were so very anxious to get rid of so short a time ago!

When we over-did the job of praising Ireland the English very naturally retaliated by asking the usual common-sense question: "If Ireland is such a grand country, why the hell did you all leave it?" Only the very simple-minded and ignorant would try to coin an answer by saying they wanted a change of air; for the world knows it is for no romantic reasons the Irish leave their country but for honest lack of bread.

The arguments were usually started to pass the time, but now and again they got very heated. When it came to that, either Cockney Jim or Murthock said something funny at the right time to save the situation. That made everyone laugh instead of striking blows, and acted like an oil on troubled waters.

One day there was a terrible hot argument going on between the English and the Irish; each side putting in as many favourable points as they could for their own country; when the quick eye of Paddy caught sight of a figure in the distance behind the English.

"In the name of the devil," said he, talking in Gaelic, "the Little Red Pudding is coming along."

Though I knew but little of that language I caught his meaning and whispered the message to Murthock who knew even less about it than I, so the three of us began to push our brushes very fast along the runway. The English, mistaking his words for the verse of a song, stood by laughing and never noticed the Walking Foreman until he was right beside them.

"What's going on here?" he asked. "Is there some'at wrong? or is nobody willing to work but the Irish?"

I glanced at my two companions, holding their hands over their mouths between every second push of the brooms, their sides shaking with laughter.

I don't know what excuse the English gave to the Foreman, but they got busy at once with their brooms, and when he was gone they told us we were mean not to tell them he was coming.

"All is fair in love and war," said Paddy with a sly wink.

"Yes then, indeed," said Murthock, "and Irish wit is often the only weapon left to fight the English with!"

Then we all had a hearty laugh and went on with our work.

It had been a glorious summer all along. I had never seen the like of it in Ireland; no rain worth mentioning for about six months since the fog lifted. The English have everything they want, I thought, including fine weather. Here I had seen empty sacks thrown about in all directions and nobody having the slightest use for them, while at home we had to pay five shillings for the sack alone before the shopkeepers would let us have the flour or meal. Many other valuable things were thrown about as well, because the English had full and plenty of their kind. I had been noticing from the start the vast riches of England. There were mills and factories working in all directions, while long lines of heavily-loaded waggons rolled along the countless railway lines from end to end of the country. The whole place seemed covered with the gloom of great industrial smoke which showed me that here was a country of vast commercial undertakings.

All this, however, had its drawbacks, because the Industrial Revolution seemed to have killed the souls of the people. They all seemed to think in the same way, leaving but little to distinguish one character from another, like so many penguins or other such birds of a feather. They did not seem to have the power of thinking for themselves, but just followed others like sheep going through a gap. We have but little industry in Ireland and little fine weather either, but thank God, we still have our individuality. Quite a lot of us can do our own thinking; and as for talking, few people ever mistake us for dummies!

I remember one Irishman, however, who, though he could talk as well as the next, did not do so, but went about his business in remarkable silence. Over here he would be looked upon as normal, but in Ireland he was "mighty odd" because he kept his mind to himself like a bonav! Because of that, people concluded that his thoughts were piled up within him, seeing that he gave none of them away. As a result they called him "Paddy the Knowledge" though he never went to college!

It was now September, and a change was coming over the weather. It started with a slight mist now and again, but that soon changed into a settled gloom and dampness. With this, a feeling of depression came over me and I could not get rid of it, no matter how I tried. The old canteen, where in early summer I had been so happy, was now pulled down, and I lamented its passing, as I saw even its very site being dug up with electric drills. Funny how we can get attached to places even in strange lands! The aerodrome was nearly finished and many of the great Lancaster Bombers, as the aeroplanes were called, had flown in to take their places in the big black hangers, or on the perimeters round about. Workers were being transferred daily to other parts of the country and the whole place got even much more lonely than it had been before. I was expecting my turn to come too at any time, for the job was being gradually finished off. Even the sweeping had come to an end, and then, to my great grief and dismay, I was transferred from the brush to the spade. I had left home twice in my life before to avoid that cursed implement, which all my relatives thought most fitting for my nature; but here I was again, back where I had started. The spade was one article I could never see any poetry in, although I was always ready to give it due credit for being like the dog, a faithful servant to mankind from the cradle to the grave; and much more so, of course, for those who had the strength to use it. Unfortunately I was lacking in that respect, so that a spade and I could never agree. Pulling together was not in our nature, I'm afraid. The spade always stood still and I had always to make the first move and do all the pushing, so we soon parted company. Now, however, I was no longer my own boss with the freedom of the hills as I had in dear old Ireland. There was not a single hill to be seen, if it went to that. I belonged to a big building firm, by virtue of my having been sent to them by the all-powerful Labour Exchange in Ely of the Isle. I had come across from Ireland with a label on me like a shoulder of bacon! The building firm paid my fare. The Royal Air Force gave me a camp to live in, a bed to lie on, and a job to work at. What more could anyone want? That was a logical argument for men with strength to use a spade, for such a thing to them was just a pleasure. They could sing and whistle as they worked, but unfortunately for me, that strength was sadly missing, so I naturally wanted something easier and better if I could get it by any means.

I did as best I could during the first day at the digging of a long drain in which pipes were to be laid, but as I knew I could not last at the job, as much from its dreadful monotony as from my lack of vigour, when the General Foreman came near us I went over and asked if he had any other job for me but this.

"I'm afraid not," he said, rather sharply; the cold look in his eyes intensified if anything.

I was just on the point of asking him another question when he spoke again abruptly.

"I'm giving you a week's notice to finish from to-day," he said, getting into his van and driving away.

Perhaps he meant this as a favour, to free me from the bondage of being attached to one firm, and give me a chance to try my luck elsewhere, but since I did not know my way about the country or where to look for a new job, I was naturally upset over being sacked in such a sudden manner. At that particular time there were thousands looking for the sack in order to get away from the particular jobs to which the over-bearing people in the labour exchanges had bound them all over the country; but I confess that I was not able to see my own dismissal in the light of a blessing in any sense. This General, in whose office I had worked, had gone off without one word of advice or encouragement to coat the bitter pill he was after giving me. My heart sank within me as I looked around the vast aerodrome where I had such mighty hopes of earning my fortune six months before. A dreary melancholy sight met my eyes, for a misty gloom was covering the Fens in all directions. The bright sun that shone so pleasantly all through the summer was nowhere to be seen. All my hopes were gone, like the smiling faces of my companions who had laughed and joked with me across the runways in the happy days gone by.

I did some very listless digging for the rest of the day, and I can assure you that when I left to go back to my hut I was in no humour for singing "A Navvy's Farewell to the Spade," though I knew well I was not returning to it on the following day, because, instead of that, I intended to go to the Labour Exchange at Ely to ask if the National Service Officer had any other job to offer me.

As I made my way back to the camp the rain came down in a slow grey lonesome drizzle which kept falling the whole night, and with it came the usual depression of spirits in all the men. In spite of that, however, they advised me what to do under my new set of circumstances, but unfortunately, nothing seemed to give me either hope or consolation. I began to feel very cowardly at the thoughts of a long winter in the mud of some other aerodrome as well, and I not fit for such a job by any means.

I slept but little that night and when I got up in the morning I prepared to go to Ely as soon as I had my breakfast taken. Though the weather was still gloomy, the rain had stopped, so I got into the Exchange with dry clothes at any rate. When the National Service Officer appeared before me, a pig could be far better-mannered than he was. The least sign of courtesy seemed as far from his make-up as I was from Ireland at the time. I thought of that dear country too, with grief in my heart, especially the lovely cultured city of Dublin, the intellectual capital of Europe, where people in offices are so polite and good-natured. The boor of Ely was such a contrast to these nice people that I could have cried with grief as he refused to help me in any way, apart from telling me to go back to my own country and that he would see to it that I did not return to England again.

I was wondering what I was after doing to harm this particular man. He was the first of the very few bad-minded Englishmen I was to know and remember. Whatever other faults the majority of his countrymen had, they were never malicious, in all fairness to the people of this land, of which he was a miserable exception. Perhaps he was after finding out by some means or other that it was I who had written to London for Michael Darcy, and here was his chance for having his own back. I felt like either jumping over the counter and making him feel what I thought about him from the clatter of my fists, or picking up an ink bottle and throwing it at him, but the grace of God kept saying to me: "Brian, my boy, keep calm. You're not at home now. You're in a strange land, so watch what you're doing. Keep an even temper. This is a heavy cross for you, but bear it patiently and, never fear, the sun will shine again when all the clouds are gone."

"May I have my cards then?" I asked, not knowing whether he or the firm I worked for had them in keeping, because I was so green about the situation.

"You won't need them, miatey," he said with a cold sneer, "for you won't be coming back."

These words struck terror into my heart. If I had to return to Ireland there would be nothing for me to do except to go to work in the bogs where the Irish Government were anxious to send as many of the unemployed as they could, so that they might be able to produce enough peat to keep the people warm instead of the coal which Britain could no longer supply them with on account of the war. The bog is surely a lovely place in which to spend a few weeks during the summer months, but the prospect of spending a long dreary winter in the same place was an entirely different matter, so I left the Exchange with a very downcast feeling, and returned to the camp to think over what was best for me to do.

Having such a big problem in front of me it was no wonder I felt puzzled and annoyed. I did not know what way to turn. Work in Ireland was out of the question. There was no implement ready there for me but a spade, only this time it was a turf-spade for a change, and if I did not take that, the neighbours would be sure to say I was lazy, because they all had strength enough to use it themselves and could not understand why I was not the same.

In the face of all this, I decided on going to London to try my luck in that mighty city, where I felt there was plenty of suitable work if I could only find it. I knew nobody there, however, but as I was after hearing many at Witchford say that there was no trouble in getting work at Handley Page's factory at Cricklewood where war materials were made in connection with the Air Offensive, I went to Ely on the following day with a heavy heart and boarded a train for London. As my head was hanging all the way with sadness I hardly noticed myself passing through the town of Cambridge which I was after enjoying so much only a few months before, and when I reached the big smoky station at Liverpool Street I was completely bewildered. I found my way out of it, however, had a meal and went off by bus to Handley Page's. I was greatly disappointed when the porter at the gate told me I could not go in unless I had an introduction card from the Labour Exchange, so off I went to the nearest I could find; and some job it was too, you may be sure, for a green Irish countryman in the world's biggest city. I found it at last, however, but, though the National Service Officer was courteous enough to me, he said he could do nothing under the circumstances as I had come from Ireland under a scheme which made me more or less the property of the firm that had paid my fare across. He had no official means of finding out my past history and he had to be extra careful owing to the war as to who he sent on a job. When I suggested the apparent willingness of the factory people in Cricklewood to take me on, he got rather excited, put on the air of a man meeting Guy Fawkes on his way to blow up the Houses of Parliament, and dismissed me curtly saying: "Certainly not to Handley Page's!"

I tried a good many other places then, but war restrictions were so tight that nobody dared to take me on without the consent of the Labour Exchange. I was rightly caught between the devil's own cursed regulations in England, and the government's own soggy old bogs in Ireland, so there was nothing I could do but return to Witchford and prepare to go back and live with my relatives in Kerry for the time being. This was a deep humiliation after all my vain hopes of being happy in England where there was plenty of suitable work if I was only allowed to do it. It was no wonder that I had no good wishes for the little pocket dictator at Ely Labour Exchange, because I felt he was the chief person preventing me from earning an honest living, for he had given me a printed piece of paper telling the authorities in Ireland that I was not wanted back.

Having sold my bicycle to George McFadden, I packed my belongings, said good-bye to my friends at the camp and, with a heavy heart, set out on the long journey home. The gloomy late September skies above the dreary Fens were in keeping with the sadness that wound itself about my soul.

Passing by the great Cathedral on my way to the Railway Station I felt very disappointed at the fate that had come over me since I first came to Ely and, stepping into the train for London I sat silently in a corner of the compartment brooding sadly over the situation. I, who had always liked a good laugh and was anxious to meet cheerful people, remained there like a lifeless log until I reached Liverpool Street. Then, after staying the night in a small but clean hotel at Euston, I went on by train for Holyhead the following day.

After going through many examinations by different officers as security precautions, I was worn out by the time the last one had finished with me, and then I dragged my heavy battered cases over the gangway into the boat.

I had only just laid them down when a familiar voice chirped up beside me. I looked around. It was Murthock Marshall!

"May the God of Mankind be praised," he said, "and is it here you are again, Brian!"

"Here I am, indeed, Murthock," said I, surprised and delighted to see him; remembering with gratitude the many times he had cheered me up before. "I hope we'll meet in heaven later on."

"Of course we will," he said, "with the help of God, because they can't keep hell going on for ever now for lack of English coal!"

"I wouldn't doubt you, Murthock," said I. "You had the good sayings ever, and more power to your brain-box."

"What are you after doing with the broom?" he piped, with a sly twinkle in his eye.

"I never again want to see it," I said, "for I think it put a silvery colour on the hair above my ears."

"I didn't notice any change in mine," he said, "for I was grey already from the cement!"

"How in the name of goodness are you getting on at all?" I asked, for I was beginning to feel myself again after a long week of misery.

"Oh, not too bad," he said, putting his hand up to his face and getting serious all of a sudden, "but my eyes are still troubling me. I'm going to stay at home for the winter. I have seen enough of England for the time being and, if I live for it, with God's help, I can go back again in the spring. Come away and we'll have a cup of tea."

"Oh, the devil carry the tea they make in these boats," I said. "I'd rather drink the moonluck from a cesspool than the cursed liquid they're so fond of using here to put suspicion on the honoured name of tea."

"Och, indeed, and sure," says he, " 'tis but the kind of drink that goes for ever with the hardness of a mouldy railway bun."

"The railway bun, is it?" said I. "That seasoned fossil of a doubtful age, more fit for cases in collections from the ancients, than for making acids on the palates of passengers. It only helps to make them home-sick for the freshness of a bakehouse, and does little for the stopping of the hunger in their throats. Let us have a mineral from a bottle now, instead of a physic from an urn that's kept waiting for the people since the dawning of the day and lonesome without sweetness till the falling of the night."

"They can't get sugar for it now, man," said he, "and if they could itself they wouldn't give it to passengers, for they know they can't go elsewhere, but content themselves with pitching them to Lucifer and all his fallen angels in the everlasting pits below."

While drinking the minerals we had a long talk about our time at the aerodrome and also discussed our plans for the future, about which neither of us had any settled ideas.

As we were talking, I saw a familiar-looking figure coming towards us. It was Mick Joyce, the man from Connemara. He sat down beside us and told us that he too was returning to Ireland for the winter. He was quite happy, he said, because he had never missed a day's work since he arrived at the aerodrome. He was still wearing the same faded brown overcoat which had made him look conspicuous in the boat six months ago, so that I concluded he had not given himself time to buy another, which he could have done so very cheaply at the second-hand stores at Ely. Then my mind wandered back to County Kerry where I had known many people who liked wearing rags instead of good clothes which they left hanging about the houses to be eaten by the moths later on. Neither they nor the Connemara man were in the least concerned about the changing fashions of the modern world, or "the latest style," in spite of the fact that they had much more money than those who were always showing off how up-to-date they were. I asked Mike if he was related to Paddy Joyce who had worked with us at the sweeping. He said he was not, but that theirs was a very common surname in the West like O'Sullivan was in the South.

There was a crowd at the bar with pints of porter in their hands while many others were sitting about the place with their drinks on the tables before them. It was not long until the drink began to have an effect and they began to burst into song. They gave us "Bantry Bay" first, "Galway Bay" next, and heaven only knows how many other bays after that, with "the River Shannon flowing" in between, but I can't remember any particular melodious voice among them. Perhaps it was my own fault, because I was not feeling well, but, however, they helped to pass the time, and soon the boat arrived at the Harbour of O'Leary's Dhoon, where I landed with a downcast feeling and said good-bye to Murthock and my other friends.

Having stayed a few days with my brothers in Dublin I went back by train to Kerry again; feeling very upset over having to return a failure after having been away for only six months. Brian O'Falvey, a cousin of mine from Slievelea, was now living with his wife in our old house at Coomlaegill, where he had the job of caretaking the farm which my father had left to my brother Killian on condition that he settled down there. I declined to give such a promise and lost my home as a result. The welcome I got from the newly-married caretakers was naturally different from what my father and mother used to give me in the past whenever I returned from my wanderings. They were dead now, God rest them, and the days of welcome were over, for they were lying in silence in the grave. The caretakers treated me well enough, but I felt I was an outsider just the same, for like "The Exile of Erin," God help us, "a home and a country remained not for me." This was brought in on me so much by the unkind remarks of outsiders as to what I should do about seeing after the farm to which I had no legal right, that I decided to leave.

I was a stranger in my father's house, and my tears of lamentation for his passing had but little time to dry before these people came to show me what to do, for their own benefit, because they thought so little of the folly of my ways compared with the dazzling wisdom of their own. So I went off with a sad heart to live with my sister and her family to the west of Denny Island's and the Mountains of Kenmare. They gave me a hearty welcome which cheered me very much, and then I settled down to wait as patiently as I could until the winter was over when I might go out again to try my luck elsewhere if my health permitted.

Oh, what a long dreary winter it seemed, with the usual cold drenching rains, fogs and dampness in general, with which that lovely country seems for ever cursed. I tried to help as much as I could around the place by picking the potatoes which my sister's husband, Jacksey MacNamara, was digging, though the dear knows, I had no interest whatsoever in farming. I also helped to bring home the turf with my nieces who were now growing up; but all my help seemed nothing towards the cost of my keep in a house where money was so very scarce. Neither Jacksey nor my sister ever grumbled about it, however, and I feel eternally grateful to them on that account. They both saw that I was run down in health of mind and body, as well as being greatly troubled about my disappointment in England, and having but so little hope for the future. My sister tried to cheer me up by telling me that I would surely be able to return to that country again, and maybe to a better job, but I always had the slip of paper which the dictator at Ely had given me, and which I took to be the copy of a message he sent to the Federation of Labour in Dublin, telling them that my services were no longer required. I was fully convinced that this would prevent me from going to England again, especially while the war was on. Then, I thought, work would get scarce once more, as it was before the war, and I would finally die in the workhouse.

"God has a plan for every man and he has one for you," said my sister, adding that by the time the spring had arrived, the slip of paper would be forgotten.

But it was no use. I could not cheer up because my strength

had almost completely gone, and what could I do in England now, even if I did get there? Each day seemed very long, so that I feared to wake up in the morning to keep company with the sadness of my thoughts till fear-forgetting sleep came over me once more at night.

Now and again I visited Coomlaegill, and it made me sad to see the many things that reminded me of the past when my parents were alive and well. The horse's winkers was still hanging on the wall before my bed and it was usually the first thing I saw when I woke up in the morning if I had stayed for the night. The buckets and pans my mother used were there too but other hands were moving them about. The lonesome feeling got the better of me so much that I always felt relieved when my visit was over.

During one of these calls I learned that poor Barney O'Loughlin was after dying. I went to his wake, of course, and it made me feel sad to see his once cheerful face so calm and still in death, when I thought of the many lovely fairy stories he told me so long ago and of the jokes which made his listeners laugh so much. May the thoughtful powers of heaven give a resting to his soul.

XII   *HOPE COMES AGAIN*

The dreary winter was drawing to an end at last and spring was on the way. Here and there in sheltered places marsh marigolds and violets were showing with the rising of the daffodils and other early flowers; but in spite of it all my spirits were still very low because I had not yet recovered my health. I went to Coomlaegill as usual, for my roots were always in it and I found it hard to stay away. One evening as I was returning I met my cousin Denny O'Sullivan from Bohereenfhadda on the road outside Kenmare. He owned the house where my grandmother was born and where the fairy visitor came on a white horse for her grandfather to play a hurling match with the dead long ago. We began talking, for he was always very friendly, and it was many a time I was after sitting down to a nice meal at his mother's table in the past, God rest her soul, and she was one of the best-hearted women I had ever met. Our conversation wandered on until it came to that of people going to England.

"Some of the fellows from around here got work on the railway over there," he said, "and I hear they are delighted with their jobs."

"Lord be praised, and how did they get there?" I asked, full of eagerness, because the thought of work on the railway seemed much more attractive than that on aerodromes where there was so much slush and dirt about the place.

"Through the Federation Agent," he said, "and you can do the same if you like. They're mad looking for men for that kind of work."

"The Lord bless you for telling me, Denny," said I, in deep gratitude for the information, because living so far out on the hills I heard but little of what was going on in the rest of the world, and that was the first ray of hope that dawned on me since I got the sack at Ely six months before. "I'll apply for the job as soon as ever I can," I added, "because I can't stay for ever sponging on my sister's home."

"That's true, indeed," said he, "for upon my soul, I suppose she has her own little family cares to look after in the times that are. But anyhow," he added, as we parted, "may the road rise with you wherever you go as a stairway leading up to great success in life."

Having found out at Kenmare when the Federation Agent would be calling, I went back and told my sister. She was delighted to see me start to hope again, and we had a long talk about my prospects during the coming summer.

When the day came at last I took the cursed note I had from the Ely dictator from my pocket and threw it into the fire. I was not going to let it trouble me any more if I could help it, for the written message on it always seemed a symbol of despair, and hope was coming now to put the sunshine in its place. I cycled off to Kenmare Labour Exchange, met the Agent and filled in the Application Form he was after giving me. I was surprised that he made no mention of my being debarred from returning to England, because I was sure he was after getting notice about me from Ely through the head office of the Federation in Dublin. Instead, he directed me to go before the medical officer in another part of the town, and that if I passed as being fit, I would get my call to England in the course of a few weeks. Keeping the best side out, I told the doctor nothing about my poor health during the winter and, to my great relief, he gave me a certificate of fitness for a railway job.

To add to my good luck, the weather began to clear up. The grey dreary blanket of fog and drizzle that seemed to cover the mountains cleared away, so that their glorious out-lines appeared once more against the clear blue sky overhead. The silvery waters of Kenmare Bay were shining at their feet, and as the sun went down its beaming made a golden pathway slant across the fairy whiteness of that mirrored sheet. Good luck, like misfortune, never comes alone, I thought, as I gathered up my belongings and prepared for another adventure beyond the boundary of these lovely scenes, because no matter how delightful they were, I knew from experience and common-sense that beauty never puts a boiling on the pot.

At last the big news came in the shape of a telegram calling me to Dublin for the final tests, and signing the necessary papers before I could be allowed to go to England. I still felt very shaky about it all, imagining many obstacles that might yet stop me from going, but strangely enough, having no fear of the bombs which were then falling like rain over that un-happy country, night after night. I would willingly face any bomb that was ever made, and hope to escape it, rather than another winter like the last, with the torture of icy feet, depressing headaches and poor health in general, from which there was no hope of relief, because the damp climate of Ireland was causing it all.

I said good-bye to my sister, her husband and family, though I was really thinking it possible that I might be back again in a few days' time if things went wrong for me in Dublin.

At Kenmare I was joined by Murty Kate of Cuishna-chillock, and we made our way together to the Railway

Station. When I saw the Station Master busily going about his business with the self-possession of a farmer quietly driving his cows into a mock-field, I wondered greatly at his cleverness.

All went well with us on the journey, thank God, and as it was arranged that the medical examination would be carried out in a hostel called the Iveagh House in the shadow of Saint Patrick's Cathedral in Dublin, we were provided with food and beds there for the night. I'm telling you, indeed, that the accommodation there was far superior to what we got in the so-called hotel in which we were lodged on the occasion of my first trip to England. A doctor examined us on behalf of the British Railways and we had our papers attended to at the same place.

When all was ready, Cook's, the tourist people, took charge of us; and very nice they were too, giving us ten shillings each, in case we had any money troubles when we arrived in the land beyond the sea.

On the following morning at Westland Row Station my doubts were still with me about being allowed on board the boat, but when I was handed my travel permit at last, I knew I was safe and that the power of Ely over me was at an end, the Lord be thanked for that.

My two brothers and my brother's wife came to see me off at the harbour, and once more I felt sad to be leaving Ireland, even though I knew I could not live there any more. As the boat pulled away from the shore I felt sadder still. I was leaving all I loved in my native land a second time and I might never see it again because of the bombing in England. I thought of Dublin with its friendly, witty, charming and good-natured people; Dublin that was great in a hundred other ways as well; Dublin that had always treated me with courtesy and kindness. As on my previous voyage I looked again at the blue hills of Wicklow where I was after spending many happy days among the people who always made me feel at home. Two lovely romantic counties, Dublin and Wicklow, so very much mixed up at all times with the tragedies and glories of Ireland! Their outlines are now growing dim for me a second time, and my heart is sinking for the loss.

"The hope that once so bright did seem, now shines for me

no more," I quoted from the old song, but there was no use in romancing now. I had to face cold facts as they were, take possession of my life jacket and prepare for any trouble that might befall the boat before it reached its destination. The weather was fine, for one thing, and we had a rather pleasant voyage. There was nobody seasick, thank God.

When we arrived at Holyhead we were put through the usual paces by the Customs and Security people as on the previous trip, and when it was all over, I thanked God that I was back again in Britain, with a fresh chance of earning my living, although at the same time I could not help lamenting for my early days in "happy, happy Ireland," as Mike of Thrawanfeerla used to call it when he sang for me so gaily long ago.

As the train steamed away for London, Murty Kate and I were sitting at a table with an Irishman who was expressing very patriotic ideas about the old country. His name was Dermot MacMahon. According to his talk he had been through many dangers for the sake of Dark Rosaleen, and he would like to meet the man who would dare to say anything against her. He was typical of many of his kind, for ever honouring Ireland with their tongues and doing the opposite with their actions. I tried to change the subject several times but he always returned to his harping on the brave deeds he had done in the past. The exploits of every other hero went pale before his own. It was no trouble for him to switch the tale from one country to another. He had equally narrow escapes in England from the bombs as he had in Ireland from the British. He was really getting me to believe that even if I divided all his boasts by seven, as I usually do when listening to people like him, he would still be at least "the shadow of a gunman." Murty said but little, and if he tried to talk at all he was soon silenced by the great boaster beside him. In one of the short intervals between the tales of his mighty deeds someone casually mentioned a camel in a slight attempt to change the trend of the talk. Then someone else wanted to know if a chamæleon was a young camel, and this finished up in an argument as to whether the chamæleon was an animal, a bird or a reptile. None of us could be sure, and

94

we had no dictionary with us to decide the matter, so we left it at that for the time being.

When we arrived in London we were taken by Cook's man to a big building like a college where we were to stay for the night. It was crowded with workmen, and after we had a fairly nice meal, with no jackdaw on the menu, we sat around for a while to wait instructions as to where we were to sleep. While we waited, someone started to play tunes on a mouth-organ. I took but little notice of the music which sounded strange to me, until I saw everybody suddenly standing up. I thought they were preparing to go out, but was surprised to find they only stood still exactly where they were, as we do at the Gospel when attending Mass. I was wondering what the devil it was all about when I found myself tapped briskly on the shoulder. I looked around. There behind me, standing like a statue of Napoleon, was Dermot MacMahon, the Irish patriot. He looked at me sternly. "Get up," he said. "Get up, man. You're in England now, you know." I was puzzled by what he meant. "What is the matter?" I asked as calmly as possible. "The National Anthem, man!" he said. "The National Anthem! Is it where you don't know the tune?" I did not. But I afterwards found that it was "God save the King!"

I had nothing whatsoever against either King or Queen, but this rather sudden change in the attitude of the Irish "patriot" astonished me. When in Ireland he was all out for a Republic and in England now he was all out for the Monarchy! I knew then that the chamæleon was a reptile!

After being shown the rooms where we were to sleep we found that our beds were made on low trestles on the floor. Murty's was next to mine, and Dermot's was at the other end of the room. We had not been lying down long when a loud wailing hooter sounded. The lights were still on, but the blinds were drawn. Everyone sat up in bed, wondering what to do, because nobody knew when a bomb would drop and bring the walls tumbling down on us. Murty Kate lay back without a word and went off to sleep in no time. But the "brave" Dermot shot out of his bed and ran to the next room. Soon, however, he was back again, shivering all over. All his boasting was gone. "Con of the Hundred Battles," who had sat in front of me in the train telling of all the exploits of a chequered career, was now fully shown up as a mere stuttering coward whose former boasting went for so much wasted wind. Many of the others were afraid to get into their beds at all as well as Dermot. We were all naturally afraid with them, but I could not see what was to be gained by running from one room to another in a case like that, so I stayed where I was, intending, no doubt, to die in my bed if the worst happened.

I could not get over the bold Dermot. He was a fine example of the boasting Irishman. I had been sick listening to men like him since the Rebellion of 1916 in Ireland. Many of them were so anxious to give the impression that they were actually in Dublin during that memorable event, that people began to wonder how that generous city was ever able to accommodate so many tourists at the time, or how every Tom, Dick and Harry, could have been notified of the event beforehand, when even the leaders were puzzled as to whether or not the Rising should take place at all at the time. Hence, to cut short the many spurious tales being told by people of this class who were so used to resting on their imaginary laurels that they had become cheeky enough to ask more modest members of their audience the question: "Where were you in 1916?" some witty person cooked up an answer for them at last. "I was under the next bed to you, my friend!" and that usually shut the boaster's mouth.

XIII   *SWANLEY*

ON the following morning, after Murty and I had a good night's rest, in spite of the sirens and the commotion they caused, we both thanked God that we had escaped the bombs. After we had had our breakfast we were told the places to which we were going; Murty to Virginia Water and I to Swanley; both stations on the Southern Railway. Parting with Murty was like cutting the last link with Ireland and Kerry in particular, but I had to be satisfied. After saying good-bye, I was taken to Victoria Station which seemed a mighty place compared with Kenmare. Instead of the one small platform in that far-away town among the lovely mountains, there were seventeen here, and each one seven times as long as the one at home. I was amazed at the sight, and the quiet easy way in which the porters went about their work. There was no excitement such as one sees at country stations in Ireland. You could step into a train bound for Jerusalem and no one would even talk to you, not to mind ordering you about with your luggage, like they do in Kerry, unless he was asked to help. Thousands of people were moving about in all directions like bees around their hives. How in the name of goodness do they all know where they are going to? I asked in my own mind. I was lucky enough to have the good man from Cook's with me, but all these people seemed to be able to get about on their own. Wonders will never cease, said I to myself.

As we stood waiting by the gate that led to Number Seven Platform I found I was to have two other Irishmen going to work with me at the same place. They were now standing beside me, and when we started talking I found they were both from Castletown Beare district. I had never met them before and, as they seemed a bit rough from the way they talked, I could not make free with them. Their outlook on life was entirely different from mine, although we were all bound for the same type of work; relaying railway lines.

A man from Swanley Station in Kent, by the name of Curley Farningham, took us over from Cook's guide, and when all was ready we boarded a train which travelled to the south-east, passing Brixton and Bromley on our way. As the train moved slowly beyond a place called Saint Mary's Cray, I wondered at the strange name and also at what I thought was the longest graveyard I had ever seen, as headstone after headstone appeared in a narrow strip of ground beside the railway. I was still wondering at everything when the train stopped at a big new station and I heard a loud clear voice sounding all over the place, saying with great emphasis:

"Swanley! Swanley! This is Swanley!
This train divides here.
Are you in the right portion?
The front four coaches for Maidstone;
The rear four coaches for Chatham and Gillingham.
Swanley! Swanley! This is Swanley!

As I stepped out on the platform I felt I could have no further doubts as to where I was. I looked around me, full of amazement. Two very long platforms stretched along the middle of a deep cutting in the earth which seemed to consist of clay mixed with chalk. A railway track ran along both sides of each platform which had overhanging canopies to keep off the rain. This covering and the pillars which supported it were painted a deep green and so were most of the trains passing by. That pleased me because it reminded me of Ireland, and I had expected them to be red in a place like England!

"Come along, Pat," said Curley Farningham, moving towards an office at the end of the platform we were standing on.

I followed him with my companions, dragging my cases with me. In the office we were introduced to the Lines Inspector, Alfred Arnold and the Sub-Inspector, Perse Amos. They were both nice and courteous to us. The big problem with them, however, they frankly confessed, was that there would be great trouble in finding us a place to live in, though the higher Railway officials had made it part of their agreement on bringing us across from Ireland that they would find places for us. The best the Inspectors could do for us at present, they said, was to let Curley, their secretary, go with us into the town and see if he could find places for us. But first of all, he should take us to Dartford, a much bigger place than Swanley, to get registered at the Food Office, report to the Police and go to the Labour Exchange for the necessary introduction cards authorising us to work on the Railway. We could leave our cases in the office till we returned. I liked Arnold and Amos from the start and have done so ever since.

Curley took us to Dartford by bus. As we went past Swanley the first thing that attracted my attention was the vast size of the fields around Hextable, a lovely village to the north, which was made extra beautiful by the millions of cultivated flowers grown there both in the open and in greenhouses. We have no fields like these in Ireland where most of the land is cut into bits and pieces.

When we arrived at Dartford I was surprised to find what a big place it was, because I never remembered having heard much about it before, in spite of the fact that every schoolboy in Ireland knew a lot about its most famous son, Wat Tyler, who led the great Rebellion of 1381 as a protest against the tyranny of the time. I thought it strange that the man should be more famous than the town, and when I asked Curley to show me the Tyler Monument he told me there was no such thing. To make up for the loss, however, he treated us decently, giving us refreshments in a public house before going to the necessary offices. Then, after spending a lot of time in waiting rooms and signing a number of papers, we got things squared out at last and, having our new ration books in our pockets, returned to Swanley Station once more.

From there we accompanied Curley to what he thought was a sure refuge, knowing no better, as green Irishmen, than to follow anyone kind enough to help us in a strange place. As we went along I noticed that the social atmosphere in Swanley was much more friendly than that of Witchford and I thought the people were very good-looking as well.

But when we arrived at the door of the house where Curley thought we might be helped, we were met by a smiling woman who suddenly put on a nasty frown when she learned that we regarded her as a landlady. She seemed greatly upset at the idea, but how could we know until she explained to Curley that she was only the local Billeting Officer! She gave him a list of houses, however, where she thought we might be taken in, and that was that, as far as she was concerned.

We lifted up our cases and, having come to the first house on the list we found that all vacancies were already filled. Going along for another mile we came to the next house where the result was the same. Then I thought of what fools we had been not to leave our cases at the office until we had first found our accommodation. Depending too much on others caused this mistake and its consequent discomforts.

A little streak of common sense began to light my path as we walked along to the next house. How, I asked myself, could any landlady take three lodgers at once? It seemed ridiculous. As the other two Irishmen came from the same district and seemed to understand each other well, I decided on leaving them to search in one direction while I went off in another, expecting a better chance of finding a bed for one than for three in any house. I made the suggestion to Curley and he agreed, being already tired of the disappointments we were all having while we stayed together.

My idea was correct. After wandering about for a little while making enquiries, I was directed to a house in Greenwood Avenue, Swanley Lane. I did not like having the word "Lane" in my address by any means because I knew my friends in Kerry would naturally conclude I was living in a low-class part of the town, as lanes in Irish towns usually are, where they become the dwelling-places of roughs, tinkers and careless broken-down farmers. But at present I could not afford to be choosey and, when I saw that Swanley Lane was actually a respectable-looking main road leading to Dartford, I took my cases along and knocked at the door of the house I had been directed to. It was opened by a small dark pale-faced woman who examined me from head to foot after she had got over the first shock of hearing an Irishman with a broad Kerry brogue ask her quietly: "Have you any vacancy for a lodger, please?"

After a lot of questions and some hesitation she finally consented to take me in. I was not at all surprised at the hesitation, because I knew that it was only a few years before that a lot of Irishmen, regarding themselves as having the monopoly of "patriotism" were terrorising her country by putting home-made bombs in people's letter-boxes and so forth, so that every Irishman who called to an English door after that was naturally taken to be an irresponsible bomber from the Island of Saints and Scholars!

I felt very happy when I saw the nice clean tidy room she gave me, but what took my fancy altogether was the magnificent bed with its thick double downy mattress and snow-white sheets. Ah, thank God, said I in my own mind, I have struck luck at last, for that bed was fit for Buckingham

Palace. The whole lot seemed a great contrast to the Nissen Hut accommodation I was given at Witchford on my last coming to work in England. Having put down my cases with a feeling of intense relief, I looked around the room when the landlady went away, and was very pleased with everything, including the view of a nice wood and flower-garden in front of the window.

After a while I was called to tea with the family in the dining-room. The landlady's husband was a nice gentle-mannered little man who, like so many of his kind, seemed only second in command to his wife. I liked him for his quiet ways as he showed me over the rows of books he had on shelves about the room. How glad I felt when I saw them! I concluded that I must have arrived in the house of some better-class people at last. They had another lodger with them too; a very refined young man who worked in one of the Hextable Market Gardens, and whom they introduced as Sydney Hylands.

That night I slept soundly in the spongy softness of the glorious bed that would coax a miser from his golden trea-sures to the peaceful slumbers of a haloed saint. I must admit that when morning came I was very lazy leaving its deep and soothing surface, with the prospect before me of having, as a life-long labour dodger, to face again the possibility of being handed a shovel or spade! Having dressed and washed, I went downstairs for breakfast, and when I told the landlady of how soundly I had slept she was greatly surprised, for at that time so many people about the place had almost lost their power of sleep on account of expecting to be killed at any time by the dreadful buzz-bombs the Germans had been sending across through the air by their own power of motion from the Continent every night for the past week. Up to then, of course, I knew little about these things. I was indeed as big a coward as any of them, but my ignorance was an advantage in this case, because it saved me from so much unnecessary worry for the time being.

AFTER breakfast, with mind and body refreshed, I went off cheerfully to the Railway Station at the appointed time for further orders. The Inspector told us that Curley would take us to London Bridge Station for examination by the Railway doctor according to regulations.

"I know London Bridge," said one of my companions, Mike from Cahermore, who did most of the talking for us; and a fine good-looking hefty fellow he was, with an engaging smile which he never failed to use for his own advantage.

"Bli' me, that's good," said Curley, who seemed from the beginning to have great faith in Mike, and little in the rest of us. "It will save me all this runnin' about."

Daniel O'Gilvie, the other fellow from Castletown Beare, stayed in the background with me while Mike went boldly forward to get the necessary papers of introduction to the doctor, and so forth, for us all. Nobody in the Station even dreamt that, from my rough ungainly appearance, I could do anything beyond laboriously writing my name. I never could look smart, even if I tried, and I remember having been asked by the postmaster at Witchford if I could write at all!

All being ready, we were shown into a train bound for Blackfriars, and warned to change at a place called Peckham Rye for London Bridge. The name "Peckham Rye" sounded quaint to me when I compared it with the "Ballys" and "Kills" of Kerry, but I said nothing about it to my companions. Having every confidence in our friend Michael we did not feel the need to worry much about words only to remember the name of the station where we were to change for our journey to the doctor's place. Wasn't it a fine thing, said I in my own mind, to be earning money as we went along on a free trip to London, enjoying the scenery through the carriage windows!

After passing many stations with queer names we arrived at Peckham Rye at last and got out. Then, directed by a porter, we went down a subway and up again to another platform where we waited for the train to take us to London Bridge. When it came along we got in and made ourselves comfortable, noticing the fine soft cushions on the seats as we did so. We started talking as usual and wondering what our new life would be like. We were very much afraid that something might go wrong, either when we went before the doctor or after we had started work. As we talked away at our leisure, the train moved from station to station. We could read the names of some when big white printed letters appeared on green boards in front of the carriage windows. When we did not see these boards we never bothered our heads to look for them. Daniel and I thought Mike knew them all, so why should we worry, who knew none of them, but follow the leader officially appointed to look after us by the authorities at Swanley!

We all began to get a little puzzled, however, when we noticed that some of the names began to repeat themselves, and we lost faith entirely in Mike from Cahermore when we suddenly looked out again and saw the name "Peckham Rye" before us a second time!

"Have they two Peckham Ryes in London, Mike," I asked, unable to hide the sarcasm in my voice.

"Well, bli' me, I reckon we've made a bloomer here," said he, blushing a little and laughing; having been much quicker in picking up the Englishman's way of talking than he was in other ways of learning, as so many of his class have been in the past when picking up the "I guess" and "I calculate" of the Yanks, thinking that their language was more up-to-date as a result. "Jump out, lads," he added, "before we find ourselves back in Swanley and make proper donkeys of ourselves!"

We got out, waited at the other side of the platform for the next train to London Bridge, making no mistake this time, because we no longer depended on Mike but on our own eyes instead.

Having found the doctor's surgery at last, we felt glad, indeed. A smart-looking boy in a neat dark uniform directed us to a waiting-room and, finding him both cheerful and courteous I said to him: "You have a grand job here."

"Grand job, is it?" he said with a good-humoured sneer. "I wouldn't be here a dia longer if I could get out of it, but the blinkin' old Liabour Exchiange waunt lat me."

"What's the matter with your job?" I asked, amazed at what he was after saying, for I thought he should be very happy in such a nice clean place and uniform instead of in the many dirty jobs less fortunate boys had to do.

"The manney 'ere ain't naw good," he said. "I wan' 'o be a plumber's mite or some'in' like that, where I can 'ave enough to spend on pictures after givin' me mom thirty shillin's a week," and he went on about his business with the air of a magnate deprived of his riches and forced to work in the salt mines of Siberia. He was the first of a long line of moaning Englishmen I was to meet later, who would not be content with their lot if they had paradise itself.

Oh, said I in my own mind, if I only had a job like his, how happy I might feel away from the dread of the spade and shovel which I was so sure of being given when I began work at Swanley.

Ever since I had met my two companions I noticed that Daniel was extremely nervous. He was shivering all over, but never seemed so frightened as now before going to see the doctor. As he was so very noticeable with the shakes, God save the mark, Mike and I thought he would never pass the examination, but our surprise can be imagined when he came out smiling and told us he was after passing first class!

It was Mike's turn next, and a calmer or healthier-looking man I never saw going on the same errand. He's only wasting the doctor's time, I thought, remembering that we had all passed two doctors already in Ireland. Regulations being regulations, however, he had to go in like the rest. I had another surprise when he came out and said the doctor had refused to pass him on account of bad nerves!

"But Mike," said I, "you're as calm as a corpse in a looking-glass as far as I can see. If it was . . ." and I stopped myself just on the point of mentioning the name of Daniel for fear of giving offence.

"If it was what?" asked Mike to my great embarrassment.

"If it was myself," said I, by way of no harm, "I would not

be surprised, but a man like you that seems to be as strong as a prize bull-dozer."

"Don't mind that at all," he said. "My sight is against me too, but I can come back in a few weeks' time to have another trial."

My own nerves were in a terrible state owing to the hard winter I was after being through. I feared going in for my test, but I had to face the music now or never. When the boy called out my name I got up in great terror and went into the surgery. I found the doctor a very nice man. He examined me after the usual fashion with the stethoscope, and then tested my sight. Before I knew where I was he politely told me I had passed, and then I returned to my companions with joy in my heart.

On our way back to Swanley the bold Mike told us in confidence that he just pretended to have poor sight for the purpose of escaping service in the army, for he had been in the country before and was afraid of being traced. Acting the blind man was easy for him, I thought, but how in the name of goodness did a man like him put shakes enough into his mighty robust frame to convince the doctor that he was nervous! It was a mystery to me, indeed.

Back in Swanley we were given into the charge of the local ganger, Ernie Mills, a fine decent respectable man, who took us along the lines under the Railway Bridge to his office in a siding near the Maidstone line. There he gave us instructions as to what we were expected to do while working as temporary plate-layers, putting great stress on the fact that we must be very careful to avoid accidents on the electric rails.

"Mind the juice rail wherever you go," he warned us, and I was to hear that advice repeated many times later on by the kind Englishmen who worked with us and understood its dangers better than we did.

He gave each of us a book of rules connected with the service, and when he told us we were to be employed removing old rails and putting new ones in their place I felt myself an imaginary engineer already and would have been very pleased with the job if it had no connection with hateful picks and shovels as well as heavy greasy sleepers; but unfortunately it had!

He showed us the implements we were to use and each of these had white rubber casing round the handle to protect the user from shock in case the iron part happened to touch the live rail by accident.

I felt as if I had been taken back to school again, for the whole thing was deeply interesting. Then, when the lessons were over, it was time to go home, and as I walked back along Swanley Lane I congratulated myself that as a typical labour dodger I had already earned two days' pay without having done a stroke of real work!

I was also beginning to like Swanley. Quite a few people talked to me of their own accord, especially when the siren sounded and they thought it might be their last chance of using their tongues, as always happens with people in case of danger. One man told me Swanley was a very healthy place to live in. Sixty years ago, he said, a Royal Commission was set up to analyse the atmosphere of different places all over the country with the result that Swanley was regarded as having the best inland air in England. I was very pleased to hear that, and indeed I must say I never got good health anywhere myself until I came to live there. I like Swanley very much and always will do so because, as well as being a healthy place, it is near enough to London when I want to go there and far away enough when I want to be outside the built-up area.

XV   *THE PLATE-LAYERS*

On my third day in Kent there was no escape from work. The labour-dodger had to face the music. We met Ernie Mills at the Station in the morning and he told us we were to be attached to what he called "The Odd Gang." Having always been considered a bit odd in Ireland I thought the English remarkably quick in finding me a suitable band of men to work with! When I mentioned this to Ernie he assured me that most of the men were semi-normal; adding with a laugh that if they were perfect they would not be on the Railway but in the Forces! He said we would be going down the line to work near Rochester.

It was the first Sunday in June and the sun was shining brightly. The country looked beautiful with its green trees and waving meadows. When we got into the train we sat among the ordinary passengers who wore glum faces and kept as silent as the grave, which is the usual custom in this part of the country. Indeed this train reminded me very much of the wakes I had seen in Kerry, where everyone wore looks of mourning on their faces. The only difference here was that there was no dead body to honour; though, the dear knows, we could all be turned into corpses any minute by the terrible flying bombs that were coming down all over the district at the time.

Sitting on the lovely soft seats, without having to pay my fare, it was no wonder I enjoyed everything in spite of the boring silence. When we reached the site the train made a special stop to let us down. Our English companions were very thoughtful, telling us to step off carefully so as to avoid touching the electric rail, because there was no platform where we alighted.

Now, instead of going to work at once as we had to do on the aerodrome, the men went towards some huts where they sat on the grass, while Neddy, the "tea-boy," a pleasant red-faced little man of about sixty, began to prepare tea.

By the cord of Saint Francis, said I in my own mind, as I sat with them, work on the railway looks good if it goes on like this much longer!

Fred Barrel, a broad-shouldered smiling Englishman, sat beside me, and I was delighted to find him jolly, witty and bubbling with good humour like an Irishman. His companions called him "Crabbie" for some reason or other, and after I had heard him give out some clever and amusing comments on everything around him, I concluded that he was "a rail crabit fellow," which is the way we have for describing people like him in Ireland. He was a most intelligent man and I was very glad to have met him. When I asked him why we did not start work at once he explained that until a certain number of trains had passed on the line we could do nothing; so the tea was being made in order to spare time, as it might not be so easy to have it later on when the work would be in full swing.

Full swing! said I in my own mind, for I did not like the words any more than the idea; but there was no escape now, and I had to be satisfied. Anyhow, I comforted myself, the sun was still shining, so, by God's grace, things might not be so bad after all, and the tea was nearly ready!

Neddy soon came along with a great steaming green drum hanging from his right hand and a big white enamel mug in his left. When he laid down the drum, all the men collected around him, and I thought of the "mihuls," or gatherings, on the bogs in Kerry when the turf was being cut. There was no tap on the drum, so each man dipped his mug into the liquid and helped himself. I felt disgusted at this, but I had to do the same myself, or go without my drink. No tea tasted good to me at that time on account of the lack of sugar, and Neddy's brew was no exception. But as we should drink something with our sandwiches, we had to be content and make the best of a bad matter.

When the meal was over, and all the trains gone by, we picked up the tools and moved along to the site where work started at last. Billy New, the foreman electrician, went to a telephone box on the side of the track and rang the power-house people, asking them to turn off the "juice," as the current of electricity was called. When this was done, the line was quite safe to work on. Billy and his men placed some short wooden blocks on the ground beside the juice rail; then, having removed its fittings, twelve men stood on each side of it, lifted it out of position with big nippers called "rail dogs," and laid it on top of the pieces of wood.

I was given a light hammer with a long handle and told to strike out the wooden wedges, called "keys," by which the rails were firmly held in position on the "chairs" or metal holders on which they rested. These chairs were firmly fixed to the heavy wooden sleepers by means of iron screws.

Secretly I congratulated myself that it was a light hammer I was after being given to work with instead of a heavy pick or shovel! There were others employed at the same job which was by no means a hard one, only that I was so damned awkward at it on account of the lack of experience.

When all the keys were struck out I was given a big spanner and told to loosen the nuts, take out the bolts and remove the fishplates which secured the rail-joints. They did not look like fish to me in any way, but simply short rectangular metal plates with four holes in them for the bolts to go through to corresponding holes in the ends of the rails, and kept firmly in position by means of the tightened nuts. Short pieces of coiled wire in the shape of horse-shoes also connected the rails by welding, and these were removed by a "set" or chisel by the "juice wallahs" as the electricians were called.

When all the fastenings were off, I was put standing with eleven men on one side of a running rail while twelve more stood facing us on the opposite side. I was told that we were to lift the rail right off the chairs and on to the side of the track. I always thought one man at each end of one of these rails could lift it, and I was greatly surprised to find that instead of two men, it took twenty-four! Each rail weighed over sixteen hundredweight, and was sixty feet long. The man opposite me picked up a pair of rail dogs and, placing the nipping ends on the rail, got me to hold one of the handles while he held the other. Each pair of men did the same all along the rail.

Perse Amos, the Sub-Inspector, stood at the far end and shouted: "Ready!" and then, after a pause: "Oick!" I did not know what that meant at first but I soon found it was an order to begin work either by lifting or pushing as a team, because no sooner had he said it than all the men squeezed the dogs on the rail and lifted it as one man from its position and about a foot away towards the side of the track. After the workers had regained their breath he shouted a second time with the same result. It went on like this until all the rail was removed into the side of the track for about a quarter of a mile. Remembering how silly I was after being to think that two men could have lifted one of these heavy rails I thought of the old Irish proverb which says: "The best hurler is always on the fence!"

It was a double track, and while we were working, a train passed by on the up-line. Before it came along, the men were allowed to smoke while waiting for it to pass. During that time I was amazed to see some of them sitting calmly on the live rail.

"Saints in glory," said I to Fred Barrel, "how do they manage to escape being killed, or at least getting a dreadful shock?"

"That's very simple, Paddy," said he, for the English always called me by that name the minute I opened my mouth to talk, even in places where nobody knew me, when they heard my Kerry brogue.

"Simple, is it?" said I. "The Lord save us, it looks nothing short of a miracle to me."

" 'Tain't no miracle, Paddy," said he. "While the ground is perfectly dry under their feet they're as safe as an 'ouse. See here," and with that he sat on the rail himself! "But," he added, "I dare not do it if the ground was wet."

"The Lord be praised for all His wonders," said I, not daring to go near it myself; thinking there might be some trick in the business about which I knew nothing.

"If you were to sit on it nothing would happen," he said. "I've never had an accident with it myself in all my time, touch wood," and he put his hand for a second on the sleeper underneath.

I was after noticing that many of his countrymen had the same way for saying things. They never said "Thank God" as we do in Ireland, but always "Touch wood." It began to dawn on me that the working-class English, however good they were in other respects, were really pagans, with no faith whatever in the God of the Christians, in spite of the fact that most of them said they belonged to the Church of England, for official purposes. The "Touch wood" reminded me that the ancient Britons worshipped the oak. Perhaps that wooden god was never wholly forgotten, except when the metal of money took its place! I'm afraid, however, that from pure need, we all became idolators where that is concerned. I thought also of the great fuss a man makes if there is a ha'penny missing from his pay-packet, while he has no regret if he misses a service in church.

"If you had rubber boots on you," Fred continued, "you could stand on these rails and nothing would happen to you whether the ground was wet or dry."

"Welcome be the will of God!" said I, in great surprise. "And how in the name of goodness can the rail know whether I have rubber boots on me or not?" I asked, completely bewildered.

"That's outside my knowledge, Paddy, I'm afraid," he said, laughing, and getting up, because the look-out man with the flags under his arm had blown a whistle to warn us that the train was drawing near.

After it had passed, work began again. Soon all the sleepers were loosened up with the picks and placed in neat stacks beside the fence. Then began in earnest the job I dreaded most on account of my lack of strength—using the pick and shovel. All the rough shingled bed of the roadway had become firmly caked and had to be loosened so that the new sleepers would fit more easily into position on it. Though the work was very hard I struggled on at it as best I could, hoping that my weakness might not be noticed among so many men. I was lucky in that respect so far as the English were concerned, but not so with the Irish, for as I worked away at full strength I heard Daniel grunting beside me now and again.

"What's wrong, Dan?" I asked in a friendly way, thinking that perhaps he was not well.

"Wrong with what?" he asked with a bitter sneer. "There is nothing wrong with me, mate."

He had already picked up the word "mate" from listening to the English and was beginning to go on from the "reckon" to the "bli' me" as well.

"But there must be something wrong," said I, lowering my voice lest the English should notice a row beginning among the Irish already, for I could see by the frown on Daniel's face that I was after offending him in some way or other.

"I reckon you know what's wrong yourself," he said in an angry voice, his face lighting up at the same time. "You don't want to work, that's what it is," he added, pushing his own shovel like a snow-plough through the shingle to show me how it was done.

"But Dan," I reasoned with him, "the others are working fine and easy for themselves, and why shouldn't I do the same when they are taking no notice of me?"

"That's what you think, matey," said he, putting emphasis on the new word he was after picking up, to make sure he had grasped it properly. "Of course they're watching us all the time," he added, throwing a shovel of shingle into the air as if to show them all what he could do.

Daniel's nerves were playing on him, poor fellow, so knowing this, I said no more but worked away as best I could and as far away from him as possible. Then, after a while I moved over to Michael who was working calmly like the English.

"Why is Daniel rushing?" I whispered to him in the quiet. "Is he afraid of losing the job or something like that?"

"I shouldn't think so, indeed," said Michael, smiling as he looked the other way so as to put Daniel off the idea that we were talking about him.

"Does he want to show off, or what's the matter then?" I asked. "Is it where he fancies himself as a great workman and thinks the rest of us are duds?"

"No, it ain't," said Michael, imitating the English. "He's just a bit high, that's all. His people are all that way, and they can't help it, I suppose, God help them. I don't blame him on that account. I guess he'll soon get over it when he's after being here a whileen more."

"'Pon my soul, he reminds me of another West Cork man that started ordering me about in Ely aerodrome when it was no concern of his," I said. "But I soon pitched him to blazes and left him there to do the lot himself."

"The blessing of God on you for it, indeed," said he. "That was the proper way to treat him."

"'Tis a good job that too many people are not like that," said I, "or the world would be a place of misery on their account."

"It is then, surely," said he, "and by the same token, the worst foreman a fellow ever meets is an Irishman, for he thinks he can never get enough out of a workman."

I knew that already both from hearsay and experience. I

was after noticing all along how calm the English were compared with the Irish. Nothing seemed to shake them. When the bombs came down around them they simply remarked, "There's another, Charlie," or "Bli' me, that was a close one"; then went on with their work as if nothing more than an apple had fallen. I was amazed at the coolness of these fine people. They were brave without being the least bit boastful about it. They did not want the war either, but they could not help being in it.

Another thing I noticed was that they were in no way prejudiced against the Irish. On the contrary, here, as well as on the aerodrome, they treated us like brothers and were extremely fair to us in all things.

The present gathering of men had come from surrounding districts such as Rochester, Maidstone, Gravesend and Sevenoaks. They always collected like that when there was a big job to do, and when it was finished, they returned to their own gangs.

When the shingle was loosened and smoothed over, we went to the side of the track and lifted up the new sleepers with pairs of big clips and laid them into position on the new roadway. These sleepers were of a deep bluish-black colour and were rather greasy to handle as a result of having been previously dipped in creosote which made them smell strongly of tar. The chairs were already firmly screwed on to them.

When all the sleepers were laid in position on the roadway, the new running rails were lifted up with the dogs and placed neatly into the lips of the chairs on them, after a few taps of the hammer here and there, where an odd sleeper was out of line with the rest and prevented the rail from falling into place at once. When this was done, a little piece of metal called an "expansion iron" was placed between the ends of each two rails.

The whistle blew for lunch and we all went off towards the huts where we had our tea in the morning. Neddy came along, smiling pleasantly as usual, with the heavy drum of tea, and we all sat down to enjoy it as best we could, because after all, even if the tea was not up to the standard we wanted, at least the weather was perfect.

I sat beside Fred Barrel again, because I enjoyed his homely wit which was such a contrast to the monotonous talk of his comrades who had only a scanty collection of words at their disposal and gave the cold shoulder to all the adjectives in the dictionary in favour of that filthy foreign one already mentioned.

"What is the name of that place up there?" I asked, pointing to a hill where I saw a few houses and what looked like a church tower among some tall trees.

"That's Cobham," said Fred. "Old Charles Dickens used to stay there long ago at a public house called The Leather Bottle, if you ever heard of it."

"I never did, indeed," said I, "but of course I've heard of Charles Dickens. We all enjoyed reading about David Copperfield when we were going to school."

"You should go up there some time to see the place," said he.

"Of course I will," said I, delighted to know that I was working near such an interesting place.

"The finest gallery of brasses in the country is in that church," he said. "You should see them and Cobham Hall as well."

"What is that?" I asked. "A dance hall, is it?"

"Not at all," he said, laughing, "but a splendid castle."

"A castle!" said I, more interested than ever.

"Yes, Paddy," he said. "A lovely building like the palace of a king, in the middle of a glorious wood like fairyland itself, with gardens all around it full of roses in the summer that would stop your mind from wandering on the thorny paths of sorrow."

"Your description makes it seem a place of haunting beauty, Fred," said I; "and a proper setting surely for the jewelleries of thought. I must go to see it sometime when the chance comes on my way."

"There's another place you should see as well," he said, "before you leave the South of England."

"Where is that?" I asked, full of eagerness to find out all I could about these interesting places.

"Hampton Court," he said. "Whatever you do, don't miss that."

"Where is it?" I asked.

"Some distance west of London," he said, "on the bank of the Thames; quite easy to get there, and well worth the trouble, I can assure you."

"I'll try to get there too if I can later on," said I. "Thanks very much for telling me about it. So few people bother doing so, that I hope you will understand how grateful I am to you."

"Oh, for nothing at all," he said; "for nothing at all."

After lunch we went back to work, and as we walked along towards the site I had a good look at the great number of barrage balloons floating across the sky in front of me, tied to the ends of long cables, and controlled by winding machinery in army lorries on the ground. Each balloon was shaped like a great elephant of silvery grey, and whenever one of the flying-bombs got entangled in the cable underneath, it stopped suddenly, twisted about in the sky, then fell to the ground, making a terrible explosion like the sudden bursting of an enormous nut, causing little damage if it fell on a field, but blowing the roofs and windows from houses if it passed the cables and fell on built-up areas, as well as shattering the walls to pieces if it fell directly on a house. In the meantime, after the cable had done its work, it would have been wrenched away, making a hole from which the gas would begin to escape slowly, causing the balloon to lose shape and make the most amusing twists and turns as it gradually floated to the ground where it finally fell like an empty sack.

When we reached the site we put the fishplates on either side of the rail-joints and bolted them through. Then we put on the nuts and screwed them firmly with the spanners, knocking out the expansion irons when we had finished, leaving about a quarter of an inch of space between the rail-ends, to cover any possible lengthening of the rails in hot weather. We put the keys between the lips of the chairs and the hollow of the rails, hammering them in firmly as we went along. After us came the juice wallahs with acetylene flames, welding the little horse-shoe cables across the gap where each two rails met so that there might be no break in the current of electricity if the fishplates loosened later on.

The gangers got busy directing the men to bring the rails as near as possible to water-level, because in some places they seemed to be lower than in others, owing to the uneven surface of the shingled roadway. A lifting-jack was got and a strong wooden handle placed in the socket so that three or four men could lever it and lift the rail to the required height while others with shovels packed shingle under the sleepers so that the rail would not sink again. This was done from end to end of the new track, the ganger stooping down and staring along each rail like a goose looking into a bottle, shouting the usual "Oick!" when he wanted the jackmen to do the lifting, until he thought they had the rail up to the proper level and the men had finished the shovel-packing under the sleepers.

Our next job was to lift the juice-rails on to the white earthenware insulation pots. I shivered when doing this, fearing that I might get a shock as people do from an electric eel, but to my great relief, nothing happened. The juice wallahs secured these rails with special clips and other fittings.

The whole road was now finished. There was nothing else to do but to tidy up any old sleepers fallen out of place near the fence where they were stacked for the time being.

The two Inspectors, Arnold and Amos, walked from end to end of the job and, seeing that everything was in order directed the men to pick up the tools and take them back to the sheds. I obeyed this order with a cheerful heart, you may be solid sure; feeling glad that my first real day's work on the railway was over, and that the pay for it would be double, on account of it being done on Sunday. Billy New telephoned the power station and the current was turned on. Then the friendly Inspectors came and warned us three Irishmen about the danger of touching the juice-rails with which we had been so familiar all day before; because they knew how easy it was for us to forget it in the great excitement of our new surroundings.

Nobody danced a hornpipe for joy that work was over, as might have happened at a mihul on an Irish bog, nor did anyone lilt a tune as Pat Mulloy would have done in Coomlaegill long ago, God rest his soul. We all just walked calmly back to the huts with the picks, shovels and other tools across our shoulders; some stepping along from sleeper to sleeper, others travelling in single file along the well-worn pathway by the side of the track.

Neddy had the tea ready when we arrived, and the usual talk went on as we sat down to drink it from the white enamel mugs the railway had supplied for the purpose.

The sun was lowering in the west and casting deep shadows between the wooded wave-like ridges of country all around us, as well as putting a shiny whiteness on the great silvery balloons above. The cuckoo and the corncrake were busy with their calling and the skylarks were not silent either. Everything seemed so peaceful and natural-looking that it was hard to believe there was a terrible war going on at the same time and that at any minute death might come upon us from the deep blue skies beyond.

When the tea was over, Neddy collected the mugs and put them aside to be washed. I watched him as he moved about among the men, talking cheerfully to them all, for he seemed to enjoy every minute of his life.

"Did you throw away the salt, Ned?" I asked, when he had everything laid aside.

"What salt?" he asked in surprise.

"Whenever there is a collection of men like this for cutting turf in Kerry," I said, "if there is any salt left over after the meals, they never bring it home, for they say 'tis an unlucky thing to do."

"I shan't throw it away," said Neddy with a sly wink and the usual smile. "I'll keep it for your tea to-morrow!"

"Tea, is it!" said I. "You mean that patent weed-killer you keep in the green drum to drug the workers on the railway line."

"I'll drug you with this," he said, pretending to throw a saucepan of dirty water over me.

We had nothing to do now but wait for the train to take us back to Swanley and, when it came rolling along at last, I wondered how many of its passengers knew that since it went down that way in the morning, a quarter of a mile of new track had been laid for its next journey out of London. I reflected also that never before had I given thought to the same thing myself during all the years I had been travelling in different trains, until I actually worked on the job and saw it being done. It is the same with other things in life. We get so used to having them, that we never think of the people who get them for us, sometimes at the risk of their lives.

We stepped into the train after climbing carefully up the chassis, and again seated ourselves among the silent passengers who stared in front of them with vacant looks in their eyes like sheep being gathered in for shearing. It was a relief when the train stopped at Swanley and I got out on the platform, feeling that I was after earning a lot of money, and learning some very useful things as well.

XVI *CHANGE OF LODGINGS*

OUR next job was placing second-hand sleepers under the old rails at a siding in Bournewood, near Swanley. This was night work. Having to wait until all trains were gone off the tracks before we could bring the sleepers from another siding further down the line, we could do nothing and, as the workers had to be assembled from the out-lying districts beforehand, we all met at the Station first to get instructions. Some of the men made themselves comfortable in stationary coaches on the siding, and as I found that I would have to stay there for four or five hours, I decided to go back to my lodgings instead, and rest in bed. Slipping quietly away, unknown to the others, I walked down Swanley Lane, got into the house and went upstairs to my room.

I was no sooner lying on the soft mattress of that delicious bed than perfect sleep without a dream took hold of me. Time, eternity and railways departed from my memory completely. In the end I believe it was the loud purring of my own snores that was after doing the safety-valve to save me from an everlasting sleep, for I started up suddenly to find that it was broad daylight. I jumped out on the floor, put on my clothes, went gently down the stairs for fear of waking the others, shut the door quietly behind me and raced back to Bournewood. The men were already working as I went up in a shame-faced manner to the Ganger, Billy Mills, and told him frankly what was after happening to me. He was the man in charge of the Odd Gang and was in no way related to Ernie of the same surname, which was quite a common one among the railway people. It was a great relief to find that he did not tell me off about what I had done, because it seems the job we were to do was not of very great importance, only one to kill time until things were ready for us elsewhere. But when I returned to the others they told me that when he found me missing he very kindly sent a party into the woods to search for me in case I had fallen asleep there and been bitten by a snake. I was thankful to them all, and decided not to repeat my offence, because that glorious bed would tempt Old Nick himself to sleep for ever in its downy hollows. I shall never forget the coaxing way it brought such peaceful slumbers to my soul and body, while the buzz-bombs roared across the heavens overhead, and sent women running to the safety of their shelters all around.

I had been about a week in my new lodgings, however, when I began to feel that all was not well. I found the dinner nicely cooked each day, but as I had a very big appetite, I wanted bread with it by way of packing. As there was no rationing in the sale of that most blessed food, which was quite cheap at the time, thank God, I thought there would be nothing wrong in asking for a slice. I got a shock, however, when the landlady, instead of giving it to me, said coldly: "We don't serve bread with dinner, Brian." After a little explanation, though, she gave me a slice in the end, but her reluctance put me thinking.

When it came to the question of washing my shirts, I was puzzled too. She said she could not do it for me, but that if I liked, she would ask the woman next door to send them to the laundry with hers. I agreed, but was surprised to find the garments done in a very short time, without the usual laundry delay, and lying in my room with a bill.

"How did you manage to get the job done so soon?" I asked, on going down to pay her.

"I did it myself," she said, quite calmly; apparently forgetting that she had previously told me she could not.

That put me thinking again. If you can do it, my lassie, said I in my own mind, so can I; so when she was after going out on the following Sunday, I took my underwear to the sink and washed them there, hanging them out to dry on the line at the back of the house as I had often done in Kerry where we had no laundries.

When she came back in the evening she said nothing, but when I returned from work on the following day and sat down to dinner she gave me a lecture in a nice polite way, telling me that she did not approve of what I had done by any means. "We don't hang out the washing here on Sundays either," she added with a sanctimonious lowering of her eyebrows to impress the pagan from the wilds of Ireland.

Things went on rather quietly for the rest of the week and I was careful not to offend her again if I could help it. I was rather surprised, however, when Sunday came around, and I looked through the window to find several of the neighbouring women hanging out their washing!

"Well, that beats the devil," said I to myself. "As sure as there's a cross on a donkey, I must be after setting a new style here for Swanley's washing day!"

When I came to the house at first the landlady and I came to an agreement about the money I was to pay her each week, but now she told me suddenly that I would have to pay five shillings more. I agreed, but concluded that she simply wanted to make things awkward for me, so I secretly decided that as soon as I got a chance I would start at the top of Swanley Lane and try every house right to the bottom to see if anyone had a vacancy for a lodger.

After I had had my dinner on the following evening I strolled out to the top of the road. I knocked at the first door, and a friendly woman opened it. When I told her my business, she said she had no vacancy, but directed me to another house in the next street. From there I was sent to a third where I was made welcome and shown over a room that was vacant. The landlady seemed a clean tidy little woman, and so was her sister who kept house with her. It was agreed that I could come to live there as soon as I had arranged to leave my present lodging.

Going back to Greenwood Avenue, I paid for my week's

lodging to the landlady there, giving her the extra five shillings.

"Are you satisfied now?" I asked, as I watched her examine the money and put it into a glass on the sideboard.

"I am," she said, a little lamely. "Are you?"

"No," said I with emphasis, "I am not."

"Have you found another place then?" she asked, quite calmly, as if she already knew about my search.

"I have," said I, without any noticeable gloating; "and I'm going there as soon as I can now."

"You must give me a week's notice first," she said.

"You can have it," said I, a little doubtful about my legal obligation in that respect, but preferring peace to an argument under the circumstances.

"I don't want it," she said rather sharply. "You can go now."

"Very well then," said I. "Thank you."

The cat and mouse game being over, to my great relief, I gathered my belongings and took them to my new lodging which I found to be much better and tidier than where I had left. The landladies there were extra kind to me, in spite of the fact that they were fond of petty regulations, such as wanting me to keep everything in its place to the fraction of an inch. They were very good-natured, however, and gave me more than my share of everything in the house. Neither of them cared much for sugar in their tea or bacon for their breakfast, and on that account I had plenty of both, which was a very good thing during a period of tight rationing.

There was one big snag in the place, however. Another lodger came to stay there at the same time, and he showed an insane dislike for me from the start. He was one of the very few Englishmen I have met with who had a most unjust hatred for Irishmen in general. It seems that in the remote past some of my countrymen had done him a wrong, so now was his chance to have his own back by trying to make things awkward for an Irishman who had never done him an injury. One of his pet ways for showing his disapproval was that during the dinner, as soon as I sat at the table, he got up from it, turned his back on me, sat on a chair in front of the fire,

stooped over the flame and began to give out a series of unpleasant grunts, which was his own special way for showing
his aversion. The landladies saw how matters stood and were
very embarrassed about it; more so than ever when, in the
act of stooping, he showed about a foot of the back of his
shirt between the top of his trousers and the bottom of his
waistcoat. They were afraid to say a word in case it started
a fight between the two lodgers. He watched every chance he
got to boycott me and turn the landladies against me so that
I might have to leave. This was a cross the Lord was pleased
to send me, and my only comfort under it was the feeling
that I had a clear conscience in so far as never having done
the slightest injury to the man who put it on me.

My working hours were very uncertain so that I had to
come and go at all times, day and night. Once I came back
very late at night and as I was preparing a meal, he got out
of bed, opened the door of the dining-room, peeped in at me,
said nothing, and shut the door again. Afterwards the landladies whispered to me that he had complained about my
using more tea than I was entitled to, because of drinking it
late at night. They both knew that I was only using my ration
and was within my rights in having tea when I returned from
work. In the end, however, we all concluded that he must
be suffering from some mysterious disease that made him ill-
natured, and on that account we tried to over-look his failings.
Happily for me, he left a few months later and his absence
brought great peace to the place.

Meantime I met Sydney Hylands, the fellow who lodged
with me at Greenwood Avenue and, like all lodgers, we had
a talk about the landlady.

"She did not like you, Brian," he said, "and I do not know
why."

"I knew she didn't," said I, "from the way she acted towards me, but perhaps she failed to understand my ways, like
so many others do as well."

As clothing was tightly rationed in those days, and I found
my garments wearing out fast, I was delighted when I heard
that people working on the railway could get extra clothing
on the production of what were called "Industrial Coupons"

which were to be had on application to the head rationing office at Dover.

I got an application form, filled it in and posted it. In the course of a few days I had an answer but no coupons. The Dover officials wanted to know what I needed the coupons for, and I thought I was after giving that information on the form. I was annoyed and lost my temper. I wrote back and said I thought their question needless, answering it at the same time in the typical Irish way by asking another:

"What do I want the coupons for, indeed?" I asked. "What do I want them for? The devil be from me, and sure you don't expect me to walk about stark naked like Adam in the Garden of England! Or perhaps you'd rather see me like Mahatma Ghandi, that landed in your country's coldness to do battle for the freedom of his land, and nothing but a knotted linen loin-cloth spread between him and the court of justice!"

I showed the letter to the landladies before sealing the envelope. They were alarmed and warned me not to send it, for if I did, I might be arrested; but I consoled them by saying that even the most coldly-formal officers sometimes had a sense of humour lurking at the back of icy faces.

I sent the message to Dover at once and damned the consequences, whatever they might be.

The officials did not fail me. They sent the coupons by return of post!

XVII   *ATTRACTING ATTENTION*

In the short time I had been working I learned many interesting things. If a tree fell on the line, it automatically put the nearest signal at the "Danger" position so that no train would run into it. I was greatly surprised at the smooth way everything worked in spite of so many difficulties.

Thick "pea-soup" fogs came often during the winter

months, making it very hard for drivers to see the signals. To get over this, especially at night, it was arranged that men re-laying the lines should sleep by day and arrive at the signal-box at night to get instructions as to where they were wanted for duty with lamps and detonators. This was called "fogging." The signal-man gave each of us a lamp with sliding coloured glasses, and a packet of detonators with instructions as to what we were to do for attracting the drivers' attention when they could not see the regular signals.

My first night on this duty was very exciting. I was sent to look after the signal in a deep cutting at the mouth of a black lonesome-looking tunnel, leading from Swanley to Eynesford. In spite of its eeriness, I tried to make myself comfortable by sitting in the fogging-box with a fine fire of coke burning in a brazier before me. I passed the time by reading now and again, which went a long way towards making me forget where I was, for, as houses and people were far away, the fairies might be near for all I knew, and at any minute might come marching out of the deep shadow of the tunnel with old Boadicea leading in a chariot of rolling knives; squabbling for diversion with the Roman Legions that she fought in earnest long ago, but leaving me a stiffening corpse from fright before the driver of a train could come along and see the tragedy!

The detonators were shaped like round biscuits, and with a distance of about six yards between them, I placed three on the running rail near the Fogging-box. When I heard the first train rumbling in the tunnel I looked at the signal. It was green, so I took the detonators off and swung my lamp with the light showing through the green glass as the train came close to me. After that two or three other trains came along and the same thing happened. All went well, thank God.

It was getting late in the night, and I was consoling myself that the worst was over, when I heard another train in the distance. I looked at the signal. It was red! I got excited. What would I do now? Leave the detonators on, or take them off?

Leave them on, you devil, you, said I to myself, suddenly remembering that they were really intended to explode and warn the driver by the noise that the signal was in the "Danger" position. Leave them on, said I, and show the driver a red light in your lamp instead of a green one!

Up I stood with my light waving beside the track, keeping well back, of course, for fear the train might hit me, and I, who was there to prevent accidents, might cause one to myself! My mind was in a hurried, worried muddle. Here I was, in a strange land, about to stop a mighty engine in a narrow cutting at the mouth of a dark and lonely tunnel! My nerves were strained to the last degree.

The train came rolling along and as it was travelling slowly I consoled myself that all would be well for it was close to me now. Eroo, with that, the Lord between us and harm, I heard an explosion that would rock the thrones of heaven! Holy Moses, said I to myself, what was that? The train is blown up, surely! The cutting began to look like the Valley of the Last Trumpet, but before I had time to make the Sign of the Cross, there was another enormous bang! By then the front of the train was just passing the Fogging-box and I could see that it was still sound. But, before I could say a word there was a third explosion and then, only then, did I realise that they were all caused by the detonators, sounding all the louder because of the narrow space!

"The Lord be praised, we're all alive," said I to the driver as he stuck out his head to talk to me, for it seems he was as anxious for conversation as myself, "and may the devil carry the sudden explosions."

"What's the matter, Paddy?" he asked.

"Matter, is it!" said I. "These blasted detonators frightened the life out of me. I never heard the like of them go off before."

"They sound louder here than anywhere else," said he, laughing. "But you'll be all right, Paddy. Don't worry. I've got smelling salts here if you want some!"

"No, thank you," said I. " 'Tis as good as any salts for me to know I have not blown you up after all!"

Then, looking towards the signal, the driver saw the green light and, after a cheerful "Good-night, Paddy," withdrew into his cab and drove the train away.

This fog lasted for three days and by the time it was cleared away I had become well accustomed to both signals and detonators.

When I had my sleep after each night's fogging I cycled around the country to look for bargains in the shops. Reaching Lewisham one evening I ran into a pocket of the thickest fog I ever saw. Cycling along very carefully I saw a policeman standing where he usually did point duty. It looked so ridiculous to be there when his signals could not be seen that I had to laugh. Having read so much about the good-humour of London policemen, I decided to put it to a test.

"Can you tell me the way out of the fog, if you please, Sir?" I asked, with a churchyard look on my face.

The London policeman was up to his reputation.

"Bli' me, Paddy," said he with a rich laugh, "I don't know where I am myself now!"

When the weather cleared up we returned to our normal work. Neddy made the tea as usual, and as I thought the milk in it was rationed very tightly, I asked if we could be allowed a little more. Not a drop, I was told. It made me feel bad having to drink the tea as it was, but I had no alternative. Meantime, however, I learned that there was a Welfare Officer attached to the Railway. Perhaps he could do something about it. Where was his office, I asked. At Waterloo Station, I was told. Very well then, said I in my own mind, I'll get in touch with him by letter as soon as I can.

When I got a chance, I took pen, ink and paper, sat down and wrote to this officer, telling him of the great shortage of milk and the hard work we had to do; adding that as Napoleon said an army marches on a full stomach, it would not be fair to expect railway men to work on an empty one! I said I was really surprised to find there was actually an officer like him on the railway at all, it looked such a neglected service. I understood his difficulties well, I added, working as he was between the devil and the deep sea; hungry men on one side crying for favours; high commanders on the other declining to grant them. I finished up telling him that if he had to buy a special cow to graze along the lines at Swanley it would pay the Railway in the end!

Having dropped the letter into the post office, I went about my business and forgot it. But a week afterwards, while working at Gravesend Station, Inspector Arnold sent for me. I thought perhaps I was after doing something wrong. I got all excited, but he laughed when he saw how embarrassed I looked.

"There's nothing to worry about, Paddy," he said. "The District Engineer wants to talk to you; that's all. He would like to see you in Tonbridge next Wednesday at one o'clock. You need not come to work that day, as your train is leaving Swanley in the morning. Change at Sevenoaks and get into a steam train for Tonbridge. You'll get a travel voucher for the journey."

"What is it all about?" I asked, feeling puzzled.

"Some letter you wrote to Headquarters, I believe," he answered with a friendly wink.

I was all excitement, of course, and delighted at the same time. In the first place I was to have a day off, and I was being given a chance to see the country by means of a free journey on the trains to and from the Engineer's office. In the second, I was after being picked out from my companions for an interview with a high official. That was an honour in itself which gave me hopes of perhaps getting something better than a pick and shovel at last.

When Wednesday morning came, I dressed in my best clothes and went to the office of Inspector Arnold to get my travel voucher. Then, with a light heart I stepped into the train for Sevenoaks. There was snow on the ground so I made myself comfortable on the soft cushion of the heated carriage among the silent passengers, for I meant to enjoy myself as much as I could. Glancing about me I saw a notice on the partition reading: "Careless talk costs lives." There is no need for such a notice here, said I in my own mind, any more than in a graveyard. I was wondering if it was the war that made the people silent. Or is it always like this, the Lord save us, war or no war? I asked myself, not daring to ask anyone else. My eyebrows lifted at the least move by any of these people. They reminded me of the "Good People" in Ireland who were said to sit in stony silence in a hall to which they carried off a living person to do some job of devilment they could not do themselves. The helper often made his escape by having holy water on his person or calling on the Name of God in his distress. Then he would relate the terrible experience of finding himself alone among the rows of silent corpses of his neighbours years dead and gone from this world. A sight, he said, that sent the icy shivers running down along his back, from looking at the sunken sockets of their eyes, their lonesome grinning faces, and the long flowing funeral shrouds that of themselves alone would make a hefty hero shudder.

Here and there I saw an oast-house with its conical top, all built of very red bricks which made a pleasing contrast to the whiteness of the snow. Everything seemed natural except the silent people beside me. Here and there one of them would leave when he arrived at a station and as he stepped on the platform with a look of disdain on his face, he would bang the door behind him as much as to say: "So much for you blinking people! That's what I think about you!" I could not help saying in my own mind that if these people shut the doors gently, without a shattering noise, it would be much easier for themselves and others. I was very anxious to ask questions about the places we passed by, but was afraid to open my mouth. Some of the people that know my habit of enquiry might surely say "The devil shut your clappers!" but that suggestion would in no way satisfy my quest for knowledge.

When the train arrived at Sevenoaks it was a relief to get away from the over-powering silence. I went to a porter and asked for information about the Tonbridge train.

"That's it there," he said, pointing to a line of coaches with a hissing engine attached.

I went across the platform and got into a non-smoking carriage. Shortly after leaving the station I began to wonder what I might learn when I arrived at the Engineer's office. I was afraid of this and that. Perhaps he wanted to tell me off about writing to headquarters; for people like him never like an underdog to complain above their heads, as was the case when Michael Darcy did so with the Ministry of Labour at Ely in the year gone by.

I was full of these fears when the train arrived at Tonbridge and I got out to ask for the office. I soon found it, and when I knocked at the door, to my great surprise the Engineer greeted me with a very pleasant smile and told me to sit down while he asked a few questions concerning a message he was after getting from Waterloo Station. My heart leapt when I heard the name, and of course I thought of Napoleon's marching armies! My hopes ran as high as those of Bonaparte, although I was very cautious on account of what I was after learning from the many disappointments previous life had given me.

"You wrote a letter to the Welfare Officer, didn't you?" he asked when I was comfortably seated, facing him at his desk.

"Yes, Sir, I did," said I; "about the milk ration at Swanley."

"Well," he said, taking off his glasses and wiping them with his handkerchief, "I'm afraid we can do nothing about that."

My heart sank, and I felt the day was lost.

"But," he added, "they were greatly impressed by your letter just the same."

"I'm glad to hear that, Sir," said I; the room seeming to grow suddenly brighter; "but I hope I did not offend anyone."

"You certainly did not," he said. "As a matter of fact the Public Relations Officer wants to see you."

"Who is he, Sir, please?" I asked, delighted at the idea of a man with such a grand title even taking the slightest interest in me.

"He's the man that directs the courtesy department of the Railway," said he, putting on his glasses again. "He tries to make it easy for passengers to get information about places they want to visit and so forth."

"He has a big problem before him, indeed," said I, remembering the silent coaches I was after travelling in, "for as far as I can see, the passengers don't want to help a lot in that respect themselves. But anyhow, what in the name of all the saints would he be wanting with the likes of me for, in any case?"

"I think he wants you to write something," said he, glancing over a paper he had before him. "I don't know exactly what it is, but if you can get to Waterloo Station next Monday at eleven o'clock he will probably tell you what he wants."

"What part is his office in?" I asked, remembering how vast these London Stations were.

"It's up a stairway near the entrance," he said. "But it might be better to ask the porters for directions when you get there. Anyone will tell you where the Public Relations Office is."

"Thank you, Sir," said I; "but will the Railway people at Swanley let me go?"

"Oh, yes," he said. "I'll see to that. You travel up to London when they tell you. Don't be afraid of anything. Your day's wages will be paid the same as if you were working at the re-laying. I hope you will have good luck up there."

"Thank you very much, Sir," said I, leaving the office and quietly shutting the door behind me.

May the road rise with you, Brian, my boy, said I in my own mind as I walked along the streets to see the town before the train arrived to take me back to Swanley, and I hope it won't be a German bomb will rise it either!

For the next few days after returning to work my heart was full of glee about my intended visit to London, and wondering what the result of it would be. I kept my mind to myself about it all. My companions were forming their own opinion about me in the meantime, and I was becoming a mystery man among them. They were kind enough, however, to hide their thoughts from me; because when the English form an opinion about a person, they are usually very cautious and slow to act upon it; so different, indeed, from some of my own countrymen, whose first impulse is to punish without a fair trial, as I was after learning from bitter experience in the past. I was rather surprised, though, when Mike from Caher-more came and whispered to me that many of the English workmen regarded me as a spy for Germany, moreover as I was in the habit of speaking fairly of the Germans when such a thing made nobody popular.

Having got my instructions from Inspector Arnold at Swanley Station, I did not come for work on Monday morning, but dressed up and went by train to London, changing to the Underground trains at Blackfriars and going from there to Waterloo. I'm telling you I got a fright at Charing Cross when I knew the train was to go under the River

Thames! What would I do, I asked myself, if the ground suddenly broke above us from a bomb, and water came in roaring torrents through the crack to drown us all! To add to my trouble, I had first of all to go down a long sloping tunnel, standing on a moving stairway, if you please; my heart fluttering at the back of my throat! I had been through a few of these deep and dreary passages since I came to London. They put the fright of the world across my heart for they reminded me of the tunnel one seems to see immediately after breathing gas before an operation! The sinking feeling made me sick, as I wondered where the moving stairways came from, and where they went to when they disappeared.

Arriving safely at the south bank of the river, however, without as much as a drop of water falling on me, I found I was in Waterloo; and there in front of me was the big Station I was looking for.

The Lord be praised, said I in my own mind, as I walked up the steps into the huge building, I'd rather meet my Waterloo here than under the water any day!

The ground was covered with snow and I went into the refreshment room for a cup of tea. After that I had a walk around the Station which I was told was the biggest in the world. I could well believe it indeed. When I looked back and thought of the little Station at Gurthagreenane I laughed when I remembered how I wondered at the great cleverness of the manly Dan from Gathaniska who did the job of Station Master, Signal-Man, Porter and Public Relations Officer, all rolled up in one! He was in the same class as me in school, and was a decent honest boy that nobody ever had a bad word for. How well he was after getting on in the world compared with me! I thought. What a wonderful fellow he was! But when I looked around me at the vast Station here I began to see what a small place Gurthagreenane was after all. I kept walking about to keep my feet warm, for there was a bitter nip in the air. I was amazed at what I saw around me. Great posters lined the walls. One of them showed a railway man marching gaily along with a mighty girder on his shoulder, and underneath him written in big letters: "Guinness for strength!" I was after seeing many Irishmen knocked out by drink in my time, and this was the first picture I ever saw

131

of anyone able to stand up at all from drinking it, not to mind going about with a girder on his shoulder! That reminded me of the poetic old Wicklow man who was found lying drunk in a wet drain by the roadside near Togher of the Hills on a bright moonlight night. Finding that he could not get up, he tried to make the best of it, consoling himself that matters could indeed be much worse. "Ah," said he, looking up to the moon with deep sympathy, "may the God of Mankind be praised for everything. I'm better off than you at any rate. You can only be full once a month, but I can be that way every night of the week!

Right in the middle of the Station, under its vast roof of glass, a house with a flat roof was built, and on top of it was a mighty jolly-looking man striding along. It was the statue of a fellow called "Johnnie Walker." There was my Johnnie, as large as life, and much larger if it went to that. He was dressed in the eighteenth-century fashion with a bright red swallow-tailed coat, its tails flying behind him in the wind, white breeches and a pair of shining black Wellington boots. I had to laugh when I saw the get-up of him; he looked so life-like, while underneath him on a board in big letters were the words: "Johnnie Walker. Born 1821. Still going strong!"

I looked at the mighty roof over Johnnie's head. How in the name of goodness did they ever put it up? I asked myself. But the sudden shrill sound of an air-raid warning took my thoughts away from it. Looking about me I saw the people running in all directions for the underground shelters. Then there was a loud explosion in the distance.

"Bli' me, there's another present from Gerry," said a voice beside me. "We must be costin' 'im some money these days, I'm thinkin'."

I was surprised to hear an Englishman talk without being first spoken to. He was a little Cockney, and I had already found that these can be very sociable people.

"Do you know," said I to him, "before that bomb came down I was often thinking what a lucky people the English were compared with us in Ireland. But now I see they have to pay a price for it."

"We're always payin' for it, Paddy," said he, smiling; "ever since our old ancestors finished wearing goat-skins, but we never get no credit for it. We had Romans, Saxons, Danes and Normans. Now we have the Germans down on top of us like a ton of bricks. But we'll survive it, Paddy. We'll survive it, and England will be England all the time."

"I suppose all your forefathers were English," I said, anxious for a conversation to pass the time.

"No, Paddy," said he, shaking his head. "My father was a Highlander that kept for ever covering us with bales of Scottish plaid. He made me wear those kilty things till I was like a bloomin' mannequin at silly sweet sixteen. My mother was Welsh, and she kept pinnin' leeks across my hat until my head was like a garland to the memory of Llewelyn's Faithful Hound. My grandmother was real Irish, though, and she was always coverin' me with flags of emerald green, showing harps and shamrocks mingling with the dawning of the day."

"I suppose you got a lot of admiration from the people of your time," I said, "and found it hard to know what race was yours, indeed."

"Hard an' all it was, Paddy," said he, with a sigh. "My father kept tellin' me not to forget the glories of King Bruce, Sir William Wallace or Mary, Queen of Scots. My mother wanted me to remember Harlech's Warriors, the Western Rebel Princes and the Land of our Fathers. My grandmother wanted me to keep in mind the honours of Brian Boru, Patrick Sarsfield and Robert Emmet."

"By the hoakey-poakey," said I with a laugh, "you were sunk in the slough of the devil's own puzzling position."

"You're tellin' me, Paddy!" he said, while a broad smile came over his face. "Bli' me, I didn't know what sort of a mongrel bastard I was at all till John Bull called me up in the last war, and then I knew for good the country I belonged to."

"You were lucky to escape with your life, man dear," said I, "after the terrible time they had in the trenches in those days by all accounts."

"I've been very lucky indeed; touch wood," he said, tapping his fingers on the side of Johnnie Walker's house.

"Come and have a cup of tea," I said to him.

"No, thank you, Paddy," said he. "I'm just waitin' 'ere for

me mite. We go to work together. At Southampton 'e lives, 'e does, an' 'e'll be here any minute now. There's 'is train just comin' in. All the best, Paddy," and away he went towards the platform at which the train was arriving.

At the appointed time I went to the door of the Public Relations Office after being directed there by one of the porters and rang the bell timidly.

"Come in," said a voice.

I opened the door and went in.

"What can I do for you, Sir?" asked a well-dressed young man coming up to the counter in front of me.

I told him my business.

"I'll see what I can do for you," said he, going into the next room, and while I waited I sat on a cushioned seat and looked around me at the posters on the walls showing different holiday places.

He soon returned with a very pleasant-faced man who invited me in to sit down and gave me a courteous welcome, just as I might get in a Dublin office under the same circumstances. The Public Relations Officer was away at present on important business, he said, and as he was his deputy he would advise me to wait until he came back. Meantime he would take me out to lunch, which I thought extremely kind of him. We had a most interesting conversation and everyone in the place made me feel at home. The better-class English, I was finding out, were much more courteous than those of the working-class, who thought of nobody but themselves, their wives and families; the rest of the world not seeming to exist for them, except for their own benefit. This man treated me to a splendid lunch in a grand hotel, where I would have felt very awkward if it had not been for my new friend helping me out of every difficulty. I hardly knew how to find words to thank him for his generosity and the honour he was after giving me, when I compared my lot with that of my companions at Swanley, shovelling snow off the lines, perhaps, at that particular time.

When we returned to the office, the Public Relations Officer had not yet come back, so to while away the time, my friend took me to another office where he introduced me to an interesting young man who had made a name for himself by publishing lists of railway engine numbers, for the collection of which schoolboys all over the country had developed a craze. His name was Ian Allen, a very courteous person to talk to, and it surprised me to think that a young man of his age could be so very successful in the publishing business.

It finally turned out that the Public Relations Officer was not able to get back at all that day, so I had to return to Swanley without seeing him, after being told that I would be called up again for an interview later on.

I was disappointed, of course, in one way, but very pleased in another, because of all the interesting things I was after learning and the nice friends I was after meeting.

In the course of a few days I was called up again, and this time when I arrived at Waterloo I was still not able to see the Public Relations Officer. He was after leaving instructions, however, and I was told what he wanted me to do. They had some guide books, it seems, which were written in a rather dry official way, and he was wondering if I could re-write them in a livelier strain. They gave me a copy of one of them and suggested that I might re-write three or four chapters of it in my own way during my spare time, and let them see the result.

This was, of course, a big honour for me, a peasant and a labourer from the wilds of Kerry, but there was a great difficulty attached to it. I was not acquainted with the places I was to describe, nor did I know enough about the needs of passengers to qualify me for the job. However, I had a try, and when I was finished I sent the manuscripts to Waterloo. Then I got another call to the office and there I was told the result of the business. I had not done exactly what they expected, they said, but as they understood my disadvantages, there was really no harm done by having a try. They apologised for the trouble they were after giving me, which was very nice of them, indeed, because there was no trouble at all on my part, the whole thing being both interesting and entertaining. Sure I was after having four lovely days of travelling about the country from Swanley to Tonbridge and London with my fares paid as well as getting the same wages as if I had been working as a navvy! I had nothing to worry about except the disappointment at finding that the whole thing was after ending up in "a bottle of smoke." A few days later, however, I had a nice letter from Waterloo thanking me for what I had done, and containing, by way of consolation, a cheque for three pounds. I was greatly pleased, of course, and what more could I want?

XVIII   *MY LAST DAYS ON THE RAILWAY*

WE were working hard one day near a place called Kemsing when Billy Mills, the ganger, gave the men leave to rest and smoke for a little while. We laid down our picks and shovels. The English talked of domestic matters:

"I says to my missus, says I: 'Look here, old girl,' says I, 'no more of that shepherd's pie, or bli' me, you'll get a black eye.' "

Comparing that with an Irishman's talk at home I had to laugh:

"I was saying to herself this morning: 'Mary,' says I, 'the darning you did on my socks gives warning you'll soon have to do it again.' "

While the others enjoyed their smoke, I had no such pleasure, so I drew a book out of my pocket and began to read, as I always did to improve my mind in spare time. I was enjoying the break from work and reading away to my heart's content when I heard the sound of heavy footsteps drawing near. I looked up. It was Billy.

"Put that blinking book away," he shouted, in a gruff voice.

My Irish temper flashed as I looked him straight in the eye.

"I'll put it away," said I, "when the others put away their pipes and cigarettes, for I have as much right to read as they have to smoke," and I kept on reading until the work began again.

Billy it seems was afraid some higher officials of the Railway might come along and see me reading. That would be a big offence, of course, being so unusual, while smoking, being so common to all classes, would not be noticed. He was not the worst of the gangers by any means, as I had reason to find out a short time after, when he was transferred to another district, and replaced by a stranger who was far less considerate to the men than he was.

We were slinging sleepers from some trucks at Eynesford later on when I found out what the new ganger was like. It seems he thought Teddy Finch, my companion, and I were not working quick enough, though actually we were doing our level best at the time.

"Come along, get them out," he shouted, as Teddy and I were in the act of lifting a heavy sleeper.

We carried on as usual without getting in the least excited, and when he was gone, Teddy thanked me for taking things so quietly, because he was not physically fit for rushing. But later on, when we got off the truck and stood talking for a few seconds, the ganger came along and told us to get on with the work. Then I flared up and told him what I thought of him in no uncertain language before all the men, and from that day forth I became unhappy at the job.

Another day as Teddy was crossing the lines he made a dreadful mistake by putting one foot on the running rail, the other on the juice rail and getting the full force of the current through his body. Luckily it did not kill him. He let out a most unearthly shriek, flung his hands into the air and fell like an empty sack on the track. The ganger and I went towards him and lifted him up, as he was not then touching the live rail. He was naturally very frightened, and I am sure the poor fellow never forgot the shock. I was alarmed too, and became determined to get away from the job as soon as ever I could.

Get out of the job! What a hope I had! That was the dream of many unwilling railway workers at the time, not because the work was too heavy but because the money was too light!

I had been a plate-layer for about six months now, and my interest in it was beginning to lag. I had been hoping that the District Engineer or my friends at Waterloo might be able to find me something better than re-laying, but it seems they

could not do so. I was getting sick and tired of the grey
monotony, day after day. Sometimes the work was very heavy
too, especially when we had to sling big sleepers into and out
of trucks in different places. As we always worked in pairs,
the strong selecting the strong, and, leaving the weak to work
with the weak as a result, the frail were expected to do as
much as the robust, and told off by the ganger if they did not
do so. I was finding it extra hard under the new ganger and
so was Teddy who should never have been sent re-laying at
all. Both he and I were watching every chance to get out of it
if we could, because we felt the work too much for us, but we
had little hope of doing so on account of the strict rules of
the Labour Exchanges.

As the Income Tax people were laying a heavy hand on
our small wages each week it was only natural that we should
be constantly grumbling about it. I heard some wonderful
stories about how some workmen tried to escape paying it.
Happy Harry, a jovial Englishman who worked with us, used
to tell about a fine-looking Irishman he knew some time previously, who was so much annoyed at the big tax he was
paying that he decided to go to the Revenue Office and tell a
tale of woe so as to avoid paying it. There was a nice innocent
girl behind the hatch when he arrived and he put on a Sunday smile when he saw her. She returned it, of course, as do
all women where good-looking men are concerned, because
they keep their frowns in freezing for unlucky devils with
uncomely faces. It was not long till this palavering Paddy
had her on the point of shedding bitter tears when telling
her about his people in Ireland, and how badly-off they were.
A lame grandmother, a simple sister, a workless landless
father and mother; and he, the man before her, their last and
only support, being bound for beggary by the taxing laws!
How could she have the heart to let things go on like that?
Of course she hadn't, and the result was that in a few weeks'
time he got off scot-free. In addition to that, he got a big
refund into the bargain.

"No wonder he could laugh then," said Harry, "for he had
neither father, mother, sister or grandmother to look after.
He was a bastard, you see, and the workhouse was the only
home he ever knew in Ireland! But his Irish blarney did the

138

trick for him. Bli' me, he had some laugh at his success with the lassie behind the counter, and a good spree out of the refund as well!"

Having heard so many stories about people getting tax relief by simply talking these counter girls into granting it, I decided on trying my luck in the same way, though I was fully conscious of my disadvantages; but when I arrived at the office I got no smile even when I tried to say funny things. I was neither good-looking enough to please the girl's eye, nor plausible enough to convince her that I really needed a reduction of tax, so she told me frankly in very cold language that she could do nothing for me and that I should go on paying the same tax as before. Perhaps, she added, I might even have to pay more when my case was properly looked into! I was slowly learning the cruel fact that people get rewarded for telling lies in this world, and punished for telling truth.

Night duty always disagreed with me. Hours of waiting in the cold air made me feel sick and depressed. When all the trains were after going by and work started, I often felt in a haze, moreover if things were in any way hurried and I had little experience of them. Billy Mills, the Swanley ganger, was with us one night and as he was always a nice helpful man, he was telling me how to do the job as he walked beside me. I was hammering home the keys where a new rail was after being laid. I hammered one and all went well. I hammered two with the same result. I hammered three or four more with Billy beside me all the time. Unfortunately, when I came across a stubborn key the hammer slipped and, instead of hitting its object, went on instead to poor Billy's shin-bone. I was very sorry and apologised as best I could, but that was a poor cure for an injured limb. Luckily it was not broken, so he moved away towards the resting-hut, moaning a lot as he went. I felt terribly ashamed of what I had done, moreover to such a decent man. It would not have troubled me half as much if the cursed old hammer had slipped on a bad ganger, but my luck would have it otherwise.

In addition to being awkward at the job, I had new troubles now. A lot of nasty boils began to torment me on the neck and arms; coming and going for months at a time and keeping me from work for many days. A swollen gland in the neck got so painful as well that I had to see the doctor about it. He was an Irishman by the name of Dawson Crawford who had always been very nice to me whenever I called to the surgery, and seemed to fuss a lot more about me than I was worth. He lanced the gland and it felt like having my throat cut. It did a lot of good, however, and the gland healed. He saw that my health was run down and that I was not fit for heavy work for the time being. I asked for a certificate to that effect and he very kindly gave it to me.

Returning to work, I tried to keep going for a little while more, as I had no idea what to do if I finished with the job. Standing in the Station at Swanley one day, waiting for a train to take me to the site, I heard my name called out. I looked around. It was Curley Farningham. I had previously told him of my intention of leaving the railway as soon as I got the chance. I thought perhaps he had some news for me, so I went over to hear what he had to say.

"Brian!" said he with a serious look on his face which made me expect something bad. "Brian! We have still a few bad gangers left. We'd be very pleased if you could use the hammer on them before you leave!"

My time on the railway was drawing to an end. I handed in my medical certificate at the office and asked for my discharge. To my great relief I got released at last and then I began to ponder as to what my next job would be.

XIX *THE BUILDING TRADE AGAIN*

At the time I finished on the Railway there was an Irish bricklayer by the name of John Murray living in Swanley who had previously been trying to persuade me to go with him for work in the building trade.

"The money there is bigger than what you get on the Railway," he said.

"But John, I can't do the hard work they want in the buildings," I said, remembering my time at the mixer and drain-digging.

"There's no hard work where I am," he said, to encourage me, "and if all goes to all, I'll get you a job making tea for the men, because I know the boss."

"That would suit me down to the ground," said I, delighted at the idea, "if I could only be lucky enough to get the job."

"Come with me to London to-morrow morning in the van," he said, "and I'll see what can be done for you."

I thought it over for a while and then I made my decision.

"Thank you, John," I said. "I think I'll give it a chance, as I have no other job at present."

So at seven o'clock on the following morning I called to where he lived, and when he was ready we went to the crossroads nearby to wait for the van which belonged to William Furlong, another Irishman living in Swanley and who, I discovered, was one of the heads of the firm I was to work for.

When the van came along, John and I got into the back and joined other workmen already seated there. As it rolled along, I found it rather interesting to be seeing new places. After we had travelled a very long distance over bumpy roads we entered the Blackwall Tunnel which runs under the River Thames from Greenwich to Poplar. I was very frightened in it, because the air was stifling from the horrid fumes of burning petrol and oil from the many motor vehicles going to and fro along the narrow road, their engines making strange and awful noises because of the confined space. I looked about as we went along, and noticed the great ventilating fans whirling around like the sails of a windmill. They impressed me greatly but seemed to do but little to cope with the smells and gas around us.

I felt greatly relieved, you may be sure, when we came out in the open air again, and passed by rows of old-fashioned houses, with vacant spaces between them here and there where the bombs had fallen. Then the van pulled up suddenly in front of a house where I saw five or six men waiting. When I heard them talking and joking with the Swanley men I knew they belonged to the same firm and that we had arrived at the office.

"I suppose there were hundreds killed here," said I to John, "when all these houses were blasted to pieces like that."

"Not at all," he said. "Very few were killed, indeed."

"How in the name of goodness did they escape?" I asked, in great surprise, for I could not understand how people could live when all the heavy masonry came down in heaps above them.

"They got warning from the wailing sirens that the cursed bombs were coming in the planes across the sea; so down they went, hell for leather, into the shelters the government was after making for them underneath."

"They were lucky, the dear knows; and God help us, I suppose a good many of them found their homes in ruins when they returned after hearing the lonesome siren sounding out the signal that the skies were clear again."

"Hundreds of them, indeed, had such a story, but they were thankful that their lives were spared while many were being blown to pieces by these horrid bombs in other places."

"What did they do then?" I asked, with pictures in my mind of what might happen in old Ireland if half this awful tragedy came rushing from the skies; and God forbid that it should, with women ullegoaning and lamenting, while men went round like lunatics with oaths of fury on their lips to call damnation on the enemy, or bawl directions to their neighbours in the wildness of their fears.

"They went about their business calmly," said John, "for the English are as cool as icicles in spite of all misfortunes, and their business at the time was searching heaps of debris for the neighbours with less fortune than themselves."

"What a pity that the Irish can't keep calm like them in times of war and tragedy," I said, "instead of losing senses in their surging rages, and regretting violent actions when their sanity returns."

"The English are a different race of people, and that's the holy all of it. They are used to having mighty wars while we have but the memory of little faction fights among ourselves."

"I think the English have their thoughts more centred on

the living than in mourning, or in writing lamentations for the dead."

"They keep thinking always of to-morrow, and leave yesterday alone for ever. That's why they stay so calm and cool and hopeful for the comforts of the future, and never get excited from the sorrows of the past."

"That's true for you, indeed," said I, reflecting on the sense of what he said. "God help us, I'm very like the Irishmen myself. What I sorely need is coolness in the region of my brain-box and a little warm leather for the comfort of my feet!"

With that the manager's van pulled up in front of us, and out of the back of it jumped as wild a set of Irishmen as ever left the Isle of Green; so wild indeed, that I consoled myself in thinking I was calm indeed myself compared with them.

The Manager went towards the door of the house, after glancing sideways at me. He put the key in the lock, opened the door and went in. John went after him and asked me to follow. As the three of us went up the half-broken stairs I could see that we were in a deserted building, for great pieces of wallpaper hung like curtains here and there along the walls and dust lay thick upon the floors and windows.

John introduced me as a new workman, and while we were talking, the General Foreman came in. He was a Sligo man with a sharp red face, and spoke kindly for a man in his position. John explained that I was not in the best of health, but was quite suitable for the job of making tea for the men.

The other workmen were, I found out later, too proud to do what they called "this old woman's job." They were like the men of Coomlaegill who would rather fast than lift a hand to make a cup of tea while there was a woman there to do it; never bothering to think about the many other jobs she had to do while they sat around the kitchen to amuse themselves, insulting her with criticism of her work, or suggesting, even believing in their ignorance, that she had nothing else to do but pay attention to the gentlemen of labour from the fields and bogs outside.

The General arranged for me to go out and get the men their food from the surrounding shops, as well as make the tea for them, and for the people in the offices. I was delighted, of course, as this was a light job which suited me very well. He introduced me to the different officials about him, and they seemed pleasant people enough. They all, with the majority of their employees, had come from the northern part of Connaught. He took me around to the different houses which the men were repairing after the war damage, and he told me to take orders from those who wanted their food bought from the shops, because many of them lived in places from which they could not bring sandwiches. This was all very nice indeed. I got to know the men and the shopkeepers. That pleased me very much.

All went well for a couple of days, and the only snag was the long journey from Swanley to Poplar, with the cold winds blowing through the chinks of the van while travelling in the open and the smoky gas annoying us in the Blackwall Tunnel. But morning after morning, as the men came to their tea in the dining-room, things went gradually wrong. The bun I got for one was stale, he said. The sandwich I got for another was rotten. The cake I got for a third was not the one he wanted. When I tried to explain how hard it was to get exactly what each man required, they would not listen, but gave out torrents of filthy abuse, which I was often compelled to answer in such quick and choice language that I turned the point of ridicule from myself to my accuser and made him the laughing-stock of the whole place.

It was the same at dinner-time. I was doing nothing to please my customers, even though I had tried my level best to do so under the circumstances, with all the food, except the bread and cakes being tightly rationed. Apart from that, I found the job very pleasant, and could not afford to complain.

The situation went on like this week after week, so that in the end I got quite used to it, and would even look forward to dinner-time, so that I could sharpen my wits by having to coin my answers in a jiffy to defend myself from charges that were anything but just, and making my tormentors be the butts of laughter in the end. Naturally they did not relish this and as a result they watched for every chance to make things awkward for me, so that in the long run I asked the General if he could find another man to buy the grumblers' food while I prepared the tea and did the other necessary jobs about the place. He agreed and sent me a helper by the name of Silk from Dartford. No sooner had he started than John Keane, an Irishman from Swanley, came along with a twinkle in his eye. "I'm a long time in the building trade, Brian," said he, "but this is the first time I ever heard of a teaboy's labourer!"

Silk from Dartford got on fairly well with me, but his father, who also worked on the firm, was still among the moaners. The tea I made was no good, he said. So to show me up, he sent a special messenger to a nearby café to bring him in a jug of tea each day at dinner-time. One time when it arrived, he turned his back for a few minutes, and John Keane dropped a big fist of salt into the jug. When the usual grumbling began about the tea I made, old Silk lifted his jug and took a long drink. Nobody said a word of course but all eyes were on him to watch the look of sudden embarrassment that should naturally come over his face when he tasted the salt. Instead of that however he put down the jug quietly, blew out a long breath of satisfaction, saying as he clasped his hands with rapture: "Ahaa! that's the kind of tea we want!"

A great burst of laughter filled the room. He never found out what caused it, but when I saw the others winking and whispering among themselves, I felt that they were saying with me: "Now we all see what that man knows about tea!"

Criticising the way I did my job was bad enough, the dear knows, but as they met their match in me so far as wordy arguments were concerned they felt they had failed in that particular line, so they thought up a new means of annoying me. Some of them openly refused to pay for the food they had eaten at my expense. I appealed to their sense of decency, if they had any, and did everything in my power to show them how wrong their methods were, but it was all no use. There were many honourable exceptions among them however, and one of the best was a Dublin man who never took off his hat at any time, even when all the others did so at their meals. He was by no means the first gentleman from that city that I was after meeting in my time because I always found them to be generous, intelligent and polite. Most of the others around him here, however, were as fine a collection of blackguards as ever I met, and it often struck me as being strange that so many of them could manage to collect around this particular firm at all. My employers, with the exception of one director, who seemed possessed by some sort of devil, were very nice to me, and though I had a big row one day with the General over some harmless joke I played in writing something ridiculous in a vein of Irish humour when he expected something very serious, I found him quite an honourable man, who had a good heart in spite of a violent temper.

The director already mentioned was often sent out in charge of different jobs and when he returned without notice he went into great rages if I had not everything he wanted laid before him. He insulted me right, left and centre, so much so that in the end I concluded that he was completely insane. One day in the middle of the dinner he came fuming into the room and started telling me off in front of the men without the least reason. His attitude amused me more than it hurt, so I said calmly: "Very well then, Hitler! Have it all your way!" That made him furious, for the Irish have a terrible dread of nicknames, moreover if they suit the people concerned, and are likely to stick to them for life, as well as to their families after them. He jumped on to the table like a spitting cat and threatened to either kick or hit me, but the others held him back. He probably thought he was entitled to regard me as a door-mat simply because he was a director in the firm for which I worked. I removed his delusions in that respect, however, as soon as I got the chance.

Having spent two months at this job I decided on going to Ireland for a holiday. On payment of seven shillings and sixpence at the Labour Exchange I was given a travel voucher covering all the journey to Kerry and back. All Irish workers in the building trade at that time could have this privilege twice a year if they wished, and I thought it a very decent gesture on the part of the English. I was very lucky with the weather because I had lovely clear days all the two weeks I was away.

When I returned, however, things did not look so bright for me in the job. The General called me aside and told me that in my absence the men had complained about the way I treated them and wanted me put off the job. Silk of Dartford had been doing it to their satisfaction in my absence, he said, and they wanted him to continue doing so.

"Don't blame me for it, Brian," he added. "They don't want you, and I can't help that."

"I don't blame you one bit indeed," said I. "The Irish always like a stranger better than their own. Maybe I'll be better off in any case when all is said and done."

"Don't worry," he said with a wink. "I'll find you a nice job tending the carpenters."

Now, though I knew they were not by any means pleased with my catering, I never thought they would go so far as to have me removed during my absence when I had no chance to defend myself, for I believed everyone enjoyed the banter we all had at meal-times. I had not reckoned with the type of people I was dealing with, although I was after having evidence enough of the baseness of their nature, so I went cheerfully off to one of the building sites with a carpenter called Peter Reynolds. He was a decent fellow and we got on well together. I had a much easier time with him and a much easier mind too than I had when trying to please my customers in their choice of food.

Time seemed to fly quite smoothly for the next few weeks, thank God, but I noticed that about every third morning there was nobody making the teas because Silk of Dartford was not there to do it. He simply stayed away from work whenever it suited him. I heard no complaints, however, when the men came into the dining-room and found no cakes or sandwiches before them, either to eat or to find fault with. Why should they complain, indeed? They had a man of their own choice on the job now, so they sang dumb, and ate their bread dry because there was no tea for them. I had great peace of mind at meal-times, and could not help having a secret giggle at the clever boys who had led themselves into such a trap, for even if they did not like me itself, at least, like all unpleasant things, I could always be relied on to be there.

Soon they began to desert the dining-room altogether and go off in search of outside tearooms for their meals. There was a general air of despondency over the place; so different from the time they could so freely fling their taunts at me and laugh at my retaliation.

I was enjoying life all the time because of my nice job with the carpenter, and wondering why the hell I had not gone in for it at first, when along came the General.

"Brian," said he, "they want you back to make the teas again."

"Well, they can go to the red devil and do without me," said I, "for 'twas a poor lot they thought about me while they had me at their beck and call, and it was not even mock politeness I had from them either but black insults and impudence for all my trying to please them."

"I understand your position," he said, "and sympathise with you. But the men are not content on the job while things are going on like this. Some of them may be leaving us and going to other jobs if this place does not suit them."

"Oh then, the devil suit them to his own convenience if they do," said I, "and some of them are no bargain on the hobs of hell itself."

"Brian," he said earnestly, "for my sake go back to the dining-room, and I'll give you my word that they'll conduct themselves in future."

Knowing some of his fine qualities, I began to think things over. Then I made my decision.

"I'll go back," said I, "for the time being, but if they start their tricks again, I'll be leaving the firm."

When I returned to the dining-room the following morning, I had a job to put things in order as before, but by tea-time all was well again, thank God. Then, wonder of wonders, there was not one word of criticism! Everything was perfect in the customers' eyes, as far as I could see. Good humour was once more restored and from then on I had a very pleasant time at my job. They had learnt a lesson to their cost, and showed far more appreciation for what I did for them now than they would have even dreamt of doing before.

"What is the cause of this great change in the men towards me?" I asked Peter Reynolds one day as he planed wood in the dining-room.

"They didn't understand you at first," he said, "and

148

thought you very slow in everything except the quickness of your wit."

"Alas, Peter," said I with a sigh, "I'm afraid fellows like me are often poorly judged by people who see nothing but perfection in themselves, and can't discern what's beyond the short horizon of their narrow little minds."

"You were a mighty puzzle to them surely," said Peter with a laugh, "and when they could not understand you very well, they thought the best way out of trouble was to start tormenting you, as all their class keep doing for ever to the harmless and simple. But," he added, looking me straight in the eye, "they all like you now. There's no doubt about that."

I was glad of this news, but I could not help reflecting on the cruel injustice of the world, and how men and women change about in their opinions like so many bits of straw being helpless in the winds that sweep across the mountains, or the tides that keep a movement in the waters of the deep.

Meantime I was after leaving my lodging in Swanley and coming to live in a hostel at Bromley-by-Bow where the old workhouse was after being damaged by bombs and repaired so that workmen could live in it after the paupers had been removed elsewhere by the London County Council. I found it a grand place indeed. The food was excellent and those who served it were the same. The management made us all comfortable, and everyone felt at home there. The majority of the residents were from Yorkshire; fine decent men, calling themselves "The Halifax Builders." Everything was very well organised.

The building was big and contained two or three recreation rooms. The beds were splendid. If the paupers had been sleeping in them once, as I was told they had, no wonder if they caused a share of envy in the minds of those that were compelled by law to keep them there in comfort by the payment of a tax!

When we got sick there was a staff of nurses to look after us. Very good they were too, and the woman who had charge of them was the only one I ever met in such a post being worthy of the name of lady as well as matron of the house. The residents would do all they could for her and she would do the same for them. I felt very glad to be there, because I wanted to live in London so that I might see some of the many interesting things in that great city. There was only one snag. The air was by no means pure because of gasworks nearby that smelled so horrid sometimes, and all the smoke from factories around the place as well.

XX   *I BECOME A HOUSE-PAINTER*

BEING still very green in the building trade I never gave a thought to the fact that when a particular job was finished, the firms no longer wanted the services of their men, but naturally got rid of them, because no firm can afford to be a worker's uncle. I found however in the course of time that certain men are kept, year in, year out, while others simply come and go. The first mentioned are the select few. They are known as "blue-eyed boys" while others are called "the casuals." The first class do what they like as a rule, and the firm overlooks it, but if others even attempt such things the firm gets rid of them. This gives the regulars an unfair advantage over the casuals who dislike them as a result, and suspect them of spying for the firm.

I was ignorant of all this of course until a friend of mine, Tom Bradbury of Swanley, came along in the quiet and whispered to me that, as much of the present firm's work in that district was finished, it might be wise for me to look around for work elsewhere as soon as I got the chance. This came as a shock, but it helped me to open my eyes and put me thinking.

Meantime something occurred which gave me still more reason to see that what he was after telling me was true, for all unknown to me, there was trouble brewing between the workers and the management. It came to a head one day at dinner-time. I was standing behind a temporary counter put up for the sale of cakes, buns and sandwiches when, all of a sudden I heard the men's voices raised in anger. The talk got louder and louder as one man snapped at another; and before I knew where I was, a terrible row was after starting, with men crashing at each other from end to end of the long tables. They fought in the fashion of Donneybrook Fair. In the middle of it they upset my counter and scattered the food all over the place. They also knocked over the Dublin man's hat which was never seen off before by anyone present. Then I saw, to my amazement, why he had always kept it on. Though quite a young man, he was almost completely bald. I felt sorry for him, because he was such a decent fellow, and I knew how embarrassed he must have felt, but I had no time for reflecting on his feelings as I tried to save the buns and cakes. I also tried to get between the fighters to calm them down, but before the row had finished, they swept along the room like a river of crazy creatures and never stopped till they went right through the big window at the back! I never found out the cause of the trouble, but as far as I could gather, petty jealousies were at the back of it. Tom Bradbury was a charge-hand with the firm and I heard that one of the workers took advantage of the riot by trying to kick him when his back was turned. Nothing worried the jovial William Furlong more than the fact that he was not there to see that particular kick being given! Anyhow, the whole thing resulted in a lot of the workers leaving, and that made the need for a teaboy less than before.

When I returned to the hostel that night I talked over the situation with my friends. One of them, an Englishman, suggested that if I had to leave my present job I should go in for painting houses.

"But how could I do painting?" I asked in alarm, looking at the neatly-drawn strip of black which separated the cream on top of the wall beside me from the deep green below.

"You can do nothing without trying," he said. "You simply dip your brush into the pot, draw it up and down the wall, and the paint will stay on of its own accord!"

I laughed heartily at this, though I was deeply interested at the same time, for I always liked the idea of painting things with fresh colours. I was full of fear, however; because painters in their white overalls looked like doctors treating patients in the shape of weather-beaten walls or plastic surgeons fixing faces in the neatness of their art. How could anyone like me go near them without feeling like a quaking quack to see them keep for ever spreading beauty from the colours in their pots!

I had the devil's own courage just the same and I felt that having a try could do no harm. If I failed, I could only be sacked, and could try again elsewhere. I was very anxious to learn, and if I could only get the chance I believed I would get on all right. I consoled myself too by thinking of the Irish doctor who was put out of a grand hotel in Dublin for being drunk and disorderly, but who told the porter as a parting shot that he "was often kicked out of better places!"

"Worse than fail can't be," said my friend. "You should be able to use the brush as well as anyone else. You can't go wrong."

"But where the devil can I start?" I asked, more puzzled than ever.

"That's no trouble," said he. "Several firms are crying out for painters at present."

"Can you tell me the address of one of them?" I asked, remembering how Mike of Cahermore used to say the same thing but never would come down to brass tacks and tell me where the cry was coming from.

"I can," he said. "Kinross and Company. Their offices are near Victoria Station. Ask for the Labour Manager when you get there."

"Thank you very much," said I, taking out a notebook and pencil to make a record of the address which he gave me in full.

Staying away from work on the following Saturday morning I took an underground train going west and when I got out at Victoria I soon found the offices.

The Lord protect us, how I shivered! I went in as boldly as I could, however, and asked the girl at the counter if I could see the Labour Manager.

"You'll find him in there," she said, pointing to a brown polished door at the end of a dark-looking corridor on my left.

I went along and knocked timidly, but there was no answer. I knocked again, much louder, though still afraid.

"Come in," said a voice.

I turned the handle, opened the door and went in.

"Well, what can I do for you?" asked a middle-aged man looking up at me after wheeling around in the pivot chair beside his desk which was covered with papers.

"I want a job as a painter, Sir," I answered, fearful of making my request in the wrong way from lack of knowledge and giving the game away on myself.

"Well," he said, in quite a business way, "we could do with a painter."

I thought he might spoil the sentence by asking, "Are you a painter?" but luckily he did not. Instead, to my great relief, he simply asked, "Have you got your identity card?"

"Yes, Sir," said I, fumbling in my pocket, taking it out and handing it to him.

"Very well then," said he, laying the card on his desk, "just wait outside for a little while and then I'll let you know."

I went out, shut the door quietly behind me, and sat on a bench, fearful now that he was getting in touch with some office by means of the mysterious numbers and letters on my identity card, for the purpose of finding out whether I was an impostor or not! Every minute I expected him to open the door, come out fuming, and tell me off for wasting his time, when I was really only a labourer! I was preparing myself for the proverbial kick for the most part of a quarter of an hour when all of a sudden the door opened quietly and he handed me my identity card with a sealed envelope which he directed me to take to the Labour Exchange.

I thanked him very sincerely with all the language I could master after my mental ordeal, and in my own mind as much for escaping the kick as for the letter, which might after all be only telling the people at the Labour Exchange what a blooming old humbug I was, and maybe asking them to do something about preventing the likes of me from wasting the time of busy Managers in future!

I put the identity card into my pocket with the air of a person harbouring a cut-throat, for I feared its numbers and letters were after telling tales on me, and when I got into the street, I looked at the envelope. It was addressed to the Manager of the Labour Exchange, without the slightest word of warning on the outside that he should be as careful of the bearer as he would of a mad dog, so I put it into my pocket also, and went back to the hostel full of excitement.

The following morning, being Saint Patrick's Day, I went for a trip to Sutton near Ely to see my cousin George MacFadden who was now married to Doris Wyandham. They lived in a nice house from the windows of which there was a splendid view of some lovely green fields. They gave me a great welcome and treated me very well. I told them about the letter and my fears of what might be in it, and then seeing the kettle boiling on the stove, I got a brain-wave. Why not open the envelope and see what was in it there and then? It would save me all this terrible prolonged suspense, and there would be no harm done. After all, nobody told me not to open it, so out the letter came. Doris laughed when she saw me hold the envelope to the steam which was puffing strongly as the flap unfolded. I took out the note and was surprised to find that it was merely addressed to the Manager of the Labour Exchange and said simply: "We have employment in our painting department for the bearer of this letter if you will be good enough to give him the necessary introduction card." It was signed by the man who had given it to me.

After being presented with a lovely pot of home-made plum jam by Doris, and saying good-bye to her and George, I returned to London. Then as soon as I got the chance I went to the Labour Exchange and handed the letter in at the Enquiries Counter. I was sent from there to an official who seemed to have some doubts about me. He asked a lot of questions about the job I intended taking up.

"Can you mix your own colours?" was one of them.

"I can, to be sure," said I, putting on the air of a qualified artist; knowing well that any old fool can mix colours! Mixing them correctly was a different matter, but then, he did not ask me about that. Reminding him of it would be like a drowning rat searching for water!

"Can you do enamelling?" he went on, like a judge in the Court of Bankruptcy when a man would have little or no assets.

"Of course I can," said I, remembering on the spur of the

moment that about twenty-five years previously I was after enamelling the frame of a rusty old bicycle in Ireland!

"You'll do," said he, taking a buff card from a wicker tray beside him and beginning to write on it.

Never say die till you're dead, Brian, said I in my own mind, still fearing that he might shoot another question at me.

"Take that to Kinross and Company," he said, drying the writing on a big sheet of green blotting-paper on the counter, and handing me the card.

"Thank you very much, Sir," said I, holding it as carefully as a beggar would a ten-pound note if he was hungry, and putting it into the inside pocket of my jacket, wondering at the same time whether his questions or my answers would be of greater value to the country! Then I walked slowly towards the door trying to put on the air of a man taking but little notice of a trifle like that, but in reality expecting every second to hear him call me back and say: "Come here, you blinking impostor! Give me that card, and go back to your shovel!"

When I found myself outside at last, I moved along carefully in case he might be after putting a detective on my track. I had to be suspicious in a place like London. Then, turning the first corner, I took out the precious card and saw that it was addressed to Kinross and Company.

"With reference to your application for a painter," it stated, "I am sending you Mr Brian O'Shannissey. Please complete and return the lower part of this card."

It was signed by the Manager of the Labour Exchange in the rubber stamp method. I was so delighted that I could have gone back and called for three cheers for him in his office or three pints in the nearest public house! Under the circumstances however I had to keep as cool as an Englishman, but being Irish, I suppose, I could not help having just one little dance on the pavement.

Two women coming along the street stared at me with fear in their eyes and turned back when they saw my capers, the creatures, just as we do in Ireland when we meet a red-haired woman first thing in the morning!

Your lucky stars again, Brian, my boy, said I to myself, as I watched them hurry away, peeping fearfully over their shoulders. You're always safe when they run away. You are indeed then, upon my soul. 'Tis only when they start running after a fellow that's he's in real troublesome danger!

My next move was to take the card to Kinross and Company; then wait for further instructions. When I arrived at the office the Manager received me kindly, looked through some papers he was after taking from a shelf behind him, and said in his usual business-like way: "Take your tools to Thirty-nine Ludgate Hill in the morning."

Tools! said I in my own mind, for I didn't think a painter needed any. A tinker did, I knew; but beyond a couple of brushes perhaps, I could not see what a painter could do with tools!

"Ask for Mr Newman when you get there," he added. "He's the General Foreman."

"Thank you, Sir," said I; my heart again fluttering in case he asked me some question I could not answer about the trade I was venturing in upon.

You may be sure that I gave a deep sigh of relief when I came out into the open air again, crossed the road and went into a café for a drink of lemonade to cool the sweat of shivers I was in.

Going back to my old firm I told them I was leaving and asked for my cards. They gave them to me cheerfully, because perhaps they were glad to get rid of me at the time. At least I saved them from the unpleasant job of having to sack me; so we parted on good terms.

Then I walked about the town for a few hours, looking at painters working here and there on the outside of houses; but the devil carry the tool could I see any of them using except a brush! A new worry began as I strolled along. Perhaps, I thought, the job I was being sent to was a very intricate one that ordinary brush painters could not do! In my wanderings I came to Blackfriars Bridge and there in front of me were some very clever fellows hanging like monkeys from the girders of the railway right over the water and painting at the same time. Holy Patrick, said I in my own mind, how could I ever do a job like that!

My heart was down at my heels when I arrived back at the

hostel and waited for my friend to return from work so that he might tell me more about the trade before I made a fool of myself at it from lack of knowledge. I waited patiently until he was after taking his dinner. Then I went up to him and asked as many questions as I could, expressing surprise and disbelief at the idea of a painter needing tools. He looked at me and laughed.

"What are you laughing at?" I asked, flushing up.

"Your greenness," he said. "Of course they need tools the same as any other tradesmen."

"What sort of tools must I get then before I start?" I asked with a feeling of dismay.

"You must get a scraping knife; a palette-board; a distemper brush. . . ."

"Wait a minute till I write that down," said I, taking a notebook from my pocket and fumbling for a pencil.

"Ready?" he asked, after I had opened the book and found a vacant page.

"Yes," said I. "H'm. Go on. But wait a while. What are you after saying? Begin again, for I can't remember what you said."

"A scraping knife," he repeated, and I wrote that down.

"A palette board," he added.

"What's that for?" I asked, after writing it down.

"Mixing plaster to fill cracks in the wall," he said, adding: "A distemper brush. . . ."

"Hold on a minute," said I, in a muddle. "What's the scraping knife for, first of all?"

"Getting off old wallpaper," said he, beginning to feel a little impatient, and it was no wonder indeed.

"Thank you," said I with as much blarney as my tongue could manage under the circumstances. "I always thought people pasted new paper over the old."

"Certainly," said he; "they did sometimes. But they may want walls painted when you get there, and then the paper must come off, you see."

"My goodness, I never thought of that," said I, feeling a bigger fool than ever. "But go on. What next?"

"The distemper brush," said he. "Have you that down?"

"No, not yet; but I will now," and I began to write like

157

the hammers of hell. "Welcome be the will of God," I added, "I always thought distempering was a woman's job."

"So it is too," he said, "in country places where the men are too damned lazy to do it."

"That's the way I feel about it myself too," said I, "with all the trouble it means; but I suppose there is no way out of it now, because 'when you 'list you must soldier' as they say in Ireland."

"Well, it's up to you, my friend," said he, again looking impatient. "We must all do something or starve."

"That's true for you, indeed," said I. "But what else must I get?" I asked, fearful lest he should say a few words about a trolley for taking all the tools about!

"Don't bother with anything else for the present," said he, to my great relief. "You'll be told what you want on the job later on."

After thanking him for his kind information I went to bed with a very uneasy mind, waking up at intervals and wondering if I was doing right in chancing my arm at a trade I liked, but knew nothing about.

However, when morning came, I put my cards into my pocket, and, after having breakfast, folded up my brown overalls and went to face the trouble. First of all I had to find a shop in which to buy the tools, as I hated going on the job empty-handed as well as empty-headed; so when I arrived at Ludgate Circus I asked a man where the nearest tool shop was.

"Round the coanah, mitey," said he, pointing to the right; but after I had travelled a good bit I could not find it.

The Englishman always says "Round the corner" but he never says which corner! Paddy says "A mile and a bit beyond the cunnockawn," and when the destination is reached, one finds the "bit" is longer than the mile and the cunnockawn! No use complaining afterwards, for all he does is laugh and say: "Man alive, the day is young yet! When God made time He made stacks of it. Sit down now till we be talking!" I often thought of this when I found myself rushing along the street for no other reason but seeing others rush before me. "What are you rushing for, Brian?" I would stop and ask myself, and I could rarely find an answer!

I got to the shop at last, however, but it was shut. A notice on the door said: "Hours of opening—9 a.m. to 5.30 p.m." That was my first disappointment, for it was now eight o'clock, and I was supposed to start on my job at that time. There was no way out of it but to wait, and when the shop opened at last I went in and bought the cheapest scraping knife and distemper brush I could get, for I thought that was the safest plan for a beginner when he was not sure of himself. I did not bother with the palette-board but chanced my luck to find something suitable on the job instead.

When I arrived at my place of work the door was open and I walked in. Three friendly men greeted me. They were not working but simply walking about and examining the condition of the building which was covered with dust and cobwebs. Evidently they had only come in a short time before me. They soon told me who they were when I told them my business. One was Jack Newman, the General Foreman, a fine good-humoured fellow, and the other two were labourers. They were all Englishmen of the quiet and modest kind. They took me around with them to see over the building, commenting on its condition as they went along, and every time they mentioned painting, my heart began to flutter, in case they asked me some simple question that I could not answer.

When we were finished going around we went out for tea at a little café at the back, and as we conversed about every-day things, I studied my companions and concluded that I was very lucky to be sent among such a nice set of men on the first morning of my launching as a decorator!

On returning to the building the General told me that, as the other painters would not be coming for some days, I might as well start cleaning down the rooms in preparation for painting later on.

There was great joy in my heart as I went upstairs to the top of the building and began to clear away the heaps of rubbish I found lying about. I kept a steady eye for money hidden in corners and at the back of fireplaces, but found none. I swept the cobwebs from ceilings and walls with the distemper brush, for I had no other at the time. Then I swept the floor and left the rubbish in a heap beside the fireplace.

I needed no qualifications for that job, which consoled me greatly. Nominally at any rate, I was a painter, and I was after arriving at the house where the real job was to be done. Now and again, however, I felt embarrassed when the labourers would apologise for not having put up scaffolding so that I could work with more ease! I did not even know from Adam what it was for! But I dare not tell them so, for the time being at least.

It was a big house and I had plenty to do for some days dusting and making the place tidy in general. I was so happy that I never felt the time go until pay-day. I still thought that perhaps the firm, after tumbling to the idea that I was a dud, would ignore my ambition to be a painter, settle the matter by simply giving me a labourer's wages, and leave it at that. Had they done so, I had but scanty means of redress. Fancy my surprise and delight, however, when I opened my packet, and found it contained a craftsman's wages! I could have danced about again as I did when the two women turned back, for I was further pleased when I saw myself described as "Painter" on the front of the packet. But I had to keep quiet of course and regard it as a matter of no concern that I got so much money for simply removing a few ancient cob-webs and a little dust during the previous week! In fact it would look far more business-like on my part if I started an argument with the pay-clerk about a missing ha'penny than to send a letter of thanks to the Manager for unexpected cash!

A real painter came to work with me in the course of a few days, and here I was lucky again, for he happened to be a nice jovial man. He could see that I knew nothing about the trade, but he was kind enough to tell me lots of useful things about it, and as I was eager to learn, I benefited from his instructions.

One day as we were washing the outside of the big windows overlooking Ludgate Hill, we started play-acting to pass the time. We were standing on trestles on the balcony with buckets of water beside us, far above the crowds of people passing to and fro along the street. I looked down and addressed them in the fashion of Anthony: "Friends, Romans, Countrymen: Lend me your ears." Then, forgetting where I was, I stepped carelessly off the trestles. As I did so, my overalls caught in the hook of the bucket-handle, and down it came, spilling the dirty water on the people passing by on the pavement. I was too much afraid to look down, so I ran into the room in fright, forgetting that there was no means of escape even that way if I was after harming anyone. Soon the General came up and said the water had fallen on a woman, but she regarded it as an accident and made no fuss about it. I felt very much ashamed of what I was after doing and was afraid also that I might get the sack over it. I had learnt my first lesson in the painting trade and from that on I was careful not to do any more play-acting on any sort of scaffolding.

After about three weeks the Painters' Foreman came to the job with five or six others all wearing white overalls. I felt a real black sheep now as I was the only one among them wearing brown. I decided however not to change my colours till I had gained some experience, though that made things awkward for me now and again when the strange painters would regard me as a labourer and start giving me orders as is the custom with some of them. The Foreman was a nice jolly man from Scotland. He came to me as I worked alone one day and started to ask questions, for it seems lots of new people without experience were coming into the trade at the time.

"Tell me, Brian," said he, "do you know much about painting?"

"The devil a much then," said I, "to tell you the truth."

"Well, you're honest about it anyhow," said he. "That makes it far easier for me than if you told me you knew all about it, and then let me down by spoiling a job. We both know where we are now, so in the meantime I'll give you a pot of green paint to put on the rails around the roof. When you have these done you can paint some pipes at the back. That will give you a chance to practise where mistakes can do no harm."

He took me to the paintshop in the basement and, having poured some green paint into a pot, handed it to me with a brush; then took me up to the roof and showed me what to do.

It was lovely sunny weather at the time and I enjoyed my first job of real painting. It was so much easier than the many rough jobs I was after doing in the past, and I knew that I was to get more money for doing it, as well as being given the chance of learning at the same time. The roof was flat and when I grew tired I stood up and looked around me. Saint Paul's Cathedral with its vast dome stood close by, and I had a good view of it from top to bottom. Beyond it to the right I could see Tower Bridge spanning the white winding River Thames with rows of houses lining its banks and black boats moving east and west upon its waters. To the left I could see right through the middle of Fleet Street which I knew to be a mighty place for gossiping on paper. Altogether I had a wonderful view in all directions which I enjoyed very much.

Meantime I got to know all the other workmen and that made the job more interesting. The house was crowded with painters, plumbers and electricians; so there was no fear of being lonely.

As the plumbers had many jobs in other parts of London, they were away for several days at a time. It so happened that the owners of the house wanted the builders out as soon as possible, and were likely to feel worried if the plumbing was behind when they came to see how things were going. They did not live in the place but always gave notice beforehand when they intended to come. On this particular occasion the plumbers were away, and the Painters' Foreman asked me to do the Firm a favour by posing as a plumber when the visitors arrived. Heavens almighty, it was bad enough, the dear knows, to be posing as a painter, but now it was ten times worse being asked to pose as a plumber on so short a notice! At least I knew what a painter's job was like but I had no idea of a plumber's because there were neither pipes nor baths where I came from in Kerry but the fine clear flowing mountain streams. The Foreman saw my trouble and helped me out of it. Holding his sides with laughter he took me into the plumbers' shop and showed me what to do. He pointed out a flat piece of lead on the bench, and handed me a polished wooden tool at the same time.

"You're the only one here that looks like a plumber," said he; "aren't you?"

"What makes you think that?" I asked, fearing that I was

after developing some mysterious disease, like dermatitis, peculiar to plumbers.

"They always wear brown overalls like yours," said he with another hearty laugh, to my great relief.

"And how in the name of goodness am I to play the plumber when I know nothing about it?" I asked, wondering if he was not playing a joke on me.

"That's easy, Brian," said he, winking and straining his jovial face to make it look serious. "When you hear these visitors coming, just start hitting that lead with the implement you have in your hand and they won't know what you're doing any more than you will yourself!"

"I'll do my best," said I, laughing. "But how on earth am I going to know when they're coming if I'm on the roof?"

"Stay here for the time being," said he. "It won't be long now till they come."

He was right, for he had only left the room a short time when I heard strange talk from people coming up the stairs. I began to tap the lead. In some places they call a job like that "swinging the lead!" I never felt more like a hypocrite in all my life; standing there like an animated statue, my hand raising and falling; fear shutting and opening my eyes like a blinking Hore-Belisha-Beacon! Women and men came into the next room and looked at me. It would not have surprised me if they went out again as soon as they saw me, not knowing what I was up too! But they did not. I kept watching them from the western end of my eye, thinking that it might be a good thing if I pretended to be deaf and dumb in addition to my other spurious qualifications, if any of them asked me a question I would not be able to answer, but with the will of God, I was lucky again and, apart from a friendly nod from one of the women who looked a bit short-sighted, nobody seemed to even notice that I was there at all.

I waited for some time after they were gone before returning to my job on the roof and, having finished the railing, decided on going out to paint the pipes which ran to another projecting roof, a storey lower down. Taking my paint and brush out through a window I put them down and went back for a pair of steps which I stood up near one of the pipes. Looking across to the opposite side of the very narrow street

I could see the people working in their offices. A man put his head out of a window and said he wished he had my job in the sunshine. A few more started talking to me as well, so that in a short time I got to know them all by sight. When I had finished the job all the workers were getting ready to go home, so I brought in my paint and other fittings for the night. Taking the pot and brush down to the basement I laid them on the bench. How shy I felt among all the men in white! I was just like an apprentice porter among the doctors in an operating theatre, but I kept my ears and eyes open all the time, so that I might learn what I could from what the professors said as well as from what they did. They talked about painting in general, mostly in slang terms, saying "Bli' me, the wallop was round" instead of simply "The distemper was thick." They talked a lot also about what they called "dead certs" for the coming races, but their conversation never went above these levels.

When we came back in the morning, much the same talk went on, while I stood by in silence, not being qualified to say anything. The Foreman gave me what he called "the finishing green" to put on the pipes I had undercoated on the previous day.

I went cheerfully up the stairs to my job, took the paint and steps through the window and began to work, resting the pot of paint on top of the steps as I did so. Having done the top of one of the pipes I came down to do the lower part and as I looked across to the window opposite I noticed a new figure among my friends of yesterday. She was a very nice-looking young girl, and her beauty took my mind a little from the watching of my job. She never even glanced in my direction, though, but just kept on pounding her fingers on the keys of a little machine on the desk before her in the same monotonous way that I kept hitting the piece of lead in the plumbers' shop. I am afraid I was paying far more attention to her work than to my own and wondering if her tapping was as meaningless as mine. I moved the steps along to paint the top of another pipe and placing the pot carefully on top of them, dipped my brush into the paint and was in the act of putting it on when I heard the whistle for the tea being sounded. Leaving the pot and brush on top of the steps

I went back through the window, rushed down the stairs, went across to the café and sat for a talk with the others as we drank our tea in comfort.

When I returned to my job I suddenly decided on lifting the steps into a new position, so that I might have a better view of the attractive young girl as I worked, for she took away my interest in the others so that I forgot about their presence as a seeming dullness came upon them like the moon would put a fading on the stars.

I never saw that girl again, for before I could lift my eyelids to stare in her direction, the minute I lifted the steps, down came the pot, right on top of my head, spilling its contents in a wet sticky slippery stream, first on my hair, then on my right shoulder and covering me with paint from that to the toes of my boots!

Saints in Paradise, what will I do now! said I to myself, feeling a terrible fool in front of all the people opposite, and having no doubt but that the nice young lady would have stopped her tapping to enjoy the scene! Worse than that again, I was afraid of getting the sack for spilling the Firm's paint which was every bit as dear as whiskey!

I went back through the window into the room to hide myself as quickly as possible, and was pondering over my sorrowful state when who should appear in front of me but the Foreman! I expected a hell of a telling off, but instead of that, to my great relief, he laughed heartily instead when he saw me. I never liked being laughed at, but in this case it was far better than being frowned on! He never said a word about the paint being spilled, but simply told me to go down to the paint-shop so that his brother-in-law, the "colour-man," might wash it off my hair and face with a liquid used as a substitute for turpentine.

Wasn't I the sight going down among all the workers! Bad manners to it! They laughed heartily also when they saw the state I was in, and I thought the best thing was to laugh with them.

"Mind how you fall, Brian," said David the electrician when he saw the rush I was in. "Bli' me, you're going along like a Green Line bus!"

When I got down, the man in the paint-shop got busy and

cleaned off the lot from my hair and face. He could do nothing with my overalls which were already stiffening, so that in the course of a few days they were like a suit of armour standing empty on their own!

That was my second big lesson in the painting trade. It taught me never again to leave a pot of paint on top of a pair of steps when I was going anywhere, even for a short time. And thus, little by little I was learning, sometimes to my cost, the new profession I was taking up.

A few days after this accident, Jack Newman, the General Foreman, called me over to him with a serious look on his usually pleasant face. I was wondering what was wrong, but he soon told me.

"Brian," said he, still keeping up the churchyard look; "we all knew you were Irish. There was no need for you to paint yourself green!"

XXI *THE WANDERING DECORATOR*

MOST of the work I did for the first few months was preparing walls and woodwork for painting. I cleared the dust from cracks in the plaster with my scraping knife. Then I mixed fine cement with water on a little board, finding this an awkward job, though it seemed very simple until I tried to do it. Sometimes the board would turn sideways and the water would flow away before I could use my knife in mixing it with the cement to make plaster. Many days passed before I learned the knack of doing this properly, but I had to keep on practising or give up the trade. After wetting the cracks well by dashing water into them from a bucket with my brush, I began to fill them with plaster until the surface was level with the rest of the wall. I felt very proud, you may be sure, when I saw the finished work, after I had drawn my brush over it a few times to smooth it out. Where the cracks were big I stuffed wet newspapers in at the back to make a foundation, then laid a rough coating of plaster over them and left it to harden for some time. Later on when it was ready, I put on another coat, left that to dry as well, and so on until I had it all brought level with the surface of the wall.

At this time the windows of many houses in London were covered with black-out paint, even though the war had been over for about a year. Our job was to get it off with scraping knives. I spent many days at this dreary work, finding it very hard to do on account of the blunt knife I was using, and being ignorant of the fact that I could have got a much sharper one at the shop. I kept wondering how my companions were able to do the job a lot quicker than I, and with only half the labour. I was afterwards amazed at how long it took me to find out the secret.

Another thing that annoyed me was the water that ran from the brush to my wrist and elbow as I washed distemper from a ceiling, but in the end a friendly painter told me how to avoid this.

"Dip your brush into the water first," he said. "Then tap it a few times on the side of the bucket to get rid of the surplus, and you'll find it running down your elbow no more."

I did as I was told and everything went right from that out. I also found that the same method applied to using a brush with paint; and thus, little by little I was learning something new each day, until the job was coming to an end. Then the Foreman told me he was sorry to say there was no more work for me on the Firm and that I would have to go. Even that was regarded as another lesson; for it showed me still more that there is nothing certain in the building trade.

After all I had nothing to grumble about. I was after becoming a real painter—in theory at any rate—though still afraid to wear white overalls in case anyone mistook me for a qualified decorator before my term of apprenticeship was finished. At least I would not be quite so green when I went to the next firm.

After getting my cards however I had some trouble in finding a new job. I tried the Labour Exchange and everywhere I could think of, within the small knowledge I had of likely places. I spent some very miserable days walking about the hostel in the meantime, and was on the point of returning to Ireland again when David Stuart, a friend of mine from County Antrim, asked me to go with him to Wanstead in Essex where he would ask the Manager of his own Firm to give me a job. I followed his advice and was given a start at once. Good luck was with me again for I was sent to work with a fine type of Cockney who was a gentleman in every respect as well as being very kind in showing me how to do my work properly. He gave me my first lesson in putting on distemper and taught me many other things too, for which I was extremely thankful.

Our Firm's work in the town was repairing houses damaged during the war, and all the people we met were nice and generous to us, so that ever since I have always liked the people of Essex. Though tea was still rationed they gave us some three times a day and made us feel at home in every house.

But as this job lasted only about two months I was soon out of work again. Nothing daunted however I went back to Kinross and Company and was re-employed by them; this time in houses around Fleet Street, a district I liked very much because of its literature, magazines and newspapers. I used to look longingly through the doors and windows of publishers' offices and printing works, wondering if I might ever see the day when I would be of the slightest interest to any of them.

There was a man representing The National Union of Painters on this job. He was called The Shop Steward. I never liked unions of any kind on account of their abuse of power, but when he asked me to join, I had no other alternative but to do so, or lose the job.

"I'll nominate you," he said, kindly enough, "and you can find some other painter in your own district to second me when you go to the branch meeting for admittance."

A friend of mine from Donegal was a member and as he lived in the hostel, he volunteered to second me. The meeting was held once a fortnight upstairs in a public house called The Seven Stars of Bromley, so he took me there the next night it was on. I gave him the entrance fee with my nomination paper to take in with him, but I had to wait outside for a long time, being given the impression that matters of great secrecy and importance were discussed which outsiders should not be allowed to know the least thing about. It seemed to me like a branch of the Ku Klux Klan!

After about two hours however my friend came out and said my application would be considered and that we should come back again at the next meeting for the final decision after the members had questioned me about my qualifications for admission.

When the big night came I went to the meeting place again and found two others waiting for the same purpose. After a long delay we were called in and put standing like prisoners in a row before our judges, all painters, each of whom was entitled to ask whatever question he liked about our knowledge of the trade, lest a wolf should slip in among the sheep! I was shivering in my boots like a medical student before a college of examining surgeons! We were lucky, however, because we were only asked a few simple questions; such as what part of a wall should be washed first with pickled water, or whether distemper should be laid on exactly like paint or not. When it was all over, I felt relieved at being allowed to sit on the same benches as the judges, but we had to wait about two hours more before we were finally told that we were admitted. Talk about a wait! I shall never forget these two hours of suffering in the thick stifling haze of tobacco smoke that never cleared away while I was there. I found it so annoying that I decided on paying my fees through the post in future and never again going into that room if I could avoid it. The whole time was spent in talking shop in the driest possible way while one by one the members went to a desk and paid their money to the secretary. There were no secrets whatsoever such as I had imagined during the period of waiting outside.

As the London County Council wanted the hostel as a rest centre for displaced families as a result of the bombing, its officials gave the residents notice to go, but provided accommodation for them in other hostels for the time being. I was transferred to a big one where about three thousand workers were living in houses evacuated during the war at a place called Onslow Square near Brompton Oratory. The rooms and bedding there were all right and the food was plentiful but so badly cooked that most of it was usually left on the plates because it was unpalatable. I regretted the excellent service we had at Bromley, but that was all over now.

The new hostel was much more central however and, as there was a lot of work going on in the West End of London at the time, it was an ideal place for a decorator to live in, as he was always sure of a job near at hand. It was close to Chelsea too—the land of bearded painters who do their work on canvas!

I soon found a job with a Welsh Firm, first at Sloane Square, then at Richmond, a lovely town in Surrey built on wooded ridges beside the winding Thames, where another man called Jim and I were employed painting a little Baptist Chapel. Every day during the lunch hour I walked about the town and liked it very much. The women who lived at each side of the chapel were very kind to us and treated us to tea like those of Wanstead.

I was in difficulties one day about getting to the top of the gable to do my painting when two of the plumbers on the job heard me say so. They kept silent at the time, but when I went out later to look at the job I saw that they had very kindly put up a bracket-scaffold and were actually doing the painting for me as well! I was very thankful to them, and indeed I found the people of Richmond very helpful at all times.

When this job was finished, the Labour Exchange soon found me another at Pimlico. All went well for me there while I was merely getting off old wallpaper but when the weather got suddenly cold and snow began to fall, the General Foreman asked me to put glass in the new windows and glaze them as well to keep out the cold. I was up against it in earnest then, because when I tried to make the putty stick to the frame-grooves, it would not stay there, but stuck to my fingers instead! I felt like a young baker making his first loaf, finding himself in a muddle from lack of experience. I did not know that if I had first painted the grooves, the putty would stick to them better, and that if I had rolled it in a little whiting or some such powder, it would not stick to my fingers instead! I was making a mess of the whole job and getting nowhere, when the General came along and saw the fix I was in. He was a very silent man but whenever he spoke he said a mouthful.

"How did you get into the Painters' Union?" he asked, after he had sent me back again to the wallpaper, like a naughty child sent home from school, after saying the usual "I won't do it any more, Sir."

"I expect they wanted the entrance fee," said I in the lamest possible manner, with all the cowardice of people for ever anxious to put the blame on others. "You have found me out fair and square, though," I added recovering my balance a little, "so the best thing I can do is to leave the Firm."

"There is no need for you to do that," said he, being really a decent fellow willing to give me a chance of learning.

I felt too embarrassed to stay however, so I asked for my money and cards, because my spirit was broken on the job through ignorance.

When the man at the Labour Exchange saw me at the counter again he lifted his eyebrows to show that my face was becoming a little too well known, and because "the old familiar faces" usually cause a lot of trouble to these officers he gave me to understand that the sooner I began to make myself scarce, the better it would be for both of us!

"I don't want to see you here again till Christmas Night," he said with a good-humoured wink as he handed me the introduction card.

I thought it a long sentence, because it was only the beginning of January at the time!

"The compliments of the season to you, then," said I, "in anticipation of that festive event!"

The following day I started on a job at Ennismore Gardens near the hostel and was lucky to find a very nice set of men to work with. Two big empty houses were being converted into government offices and there was a lot of work to do there for carpenters, plumbers, electricians and painters. There was plenty of glazing to be done also, and I shivered when I thought of it. The painters' Foreman was doing it himself at the time, but after a few days a special glazier came to do the job. He was only eighteen years old but he was so skilful and quick at it that the Foreman gave him charge of all the windows needing attention, and got the Firm to pay him the full rate for it as well. He soon became very popular with everyone, and with me in particular, for he seemed to be an artist in a job that I could never do. His name was Billy Deade. He was the cleverest boy with his hands that I ever met in this country and glazing came as easy to him as talking does to me. There was no job connected with the building trade that he could not do if he got the notion. He was honest and generous too. Every evening he took me on the back of his motor bicycle to the hostel which he passed on his way home to Chiswick.

I learned a lot of new things about painting in this job. The Foreman was nice and quiet; always ready to help anyone in need, and that made things easy for me. He was the first person to tell me that each part of a panel door had a particular name: style, rail, panel and so forth. I got a lot of practise putting on distemper also, because it was used a lot at that time on account of the scarcity of paint.

There was a beautiful painted ceiling in one of the rooms. It had a circular design covering most of it, showing angels, lakes and flowers. Our job was to wash it over carefully with soft soapy water and dry it off with clean cloths. I enjoyed that sort of work, because it was so easy and interesting. Soon I began to wonder why I had stayed so long on other jobs, or feared getting the sack from them when it might only pave the way to a lovely place like this!

Snow continued to fall for most of the week since I had left the job at Pimlico, and it was followed by a great frost which never left the ground for three months, so I thought myself very lucky to be in a place where we had nice fires burning in the rooms while at work.

I had been about eleven months in the painting trade now, so I got myself a suit of white overalls at last and felt very proud in them indeed, thinking that I looked like a doctor! But after that job was finished I had to leave, because the firm had no more work for me. Then began the wandering from one firm to another, during which time I learned how the same work was done by different people in different ways, so that the very wandering was a lesson in itself.

In the course of my travels I worked with several types of men, mostly Cockneys, and never had any trouble with them. But whenever an Irishman came to work with me, it was a different story, I'm sorry to say. Most of them seemed to conclude when they saw me and heard my crude Kerry brogue that they were naturally my superiors, so they began at once to convince me of it. If I said, quite casually, that the colour on a wall was light brown, they corrected me at once by telling me it was no such thing, but dark cream! If I happened to have said at first that it was actually dark cream, they would look at me in disdain, call me a fool, and say it was light brown! In the course of time I got to know their type so well that I stopped saying anything. They concluded then that I was a complete dud who needed enlightenment, and they began at once to teach me. Even young men of less than half my age considered themselves fully qualified in this respect, and when I lost my temper with them and asked what they thought I was doing during the twenty years or so before they were born, they still went on to tell me I had not even lived because I knew nothing of the things they happened to be interested in, such as football and "dead certs." I "only existed" they said, flattering themselves that as they were born clever by nature they had no need to learn anything, because their office in life was to teach ignorant people like me. Some of them were downright insulting, and did not seem to feel happy unless they were. If I began the day by saying nothing at all that might lead to an argument, they kept on saying things themselves, and looked at me with eager faces for comments. If I still said nothing, they nudged me till finally I had to say something for the sake of peace. They were off on top gear then, telling me I was wrong. Many of them were so troublesome that they caused me to leave good firms. If there were fifty men on a job and I was working peacefully with them for a few months, all would be well until an Irishman appeared. Then the foreman would think he was doing both of us a favour by sending us to work together, so he would take me away from a peaceful Cockney and put me side by side with a sneering Irishman. That was just like an inexperienced electrician putting the wrong wires together, making a flash and putting out the lights.

On the other hand, if I had the good luck to meet a decent Irishman, as I did on a few occasions, the foreman would then come along and be perverse enough to part the two of us, moreover if he heard us talk too much at work. I have met some fine decent respectable Irishmen in my own country, but alas, I am afraid they are a class that never come to paint houses in England. The fellows who do have always made it their business to get me into trouble if they can; and the strange thing about it is that they are as nice as can be when they work with the English, so much so that when I mention about the way they treat me, it won't be believed that such "nice" Irishmen can act that way towards their own countrymen. An Englishman may not be able to talk properly, or even write his name, but the minute he opens his mouth to say anything, these admiring Irishmen are sure to give him wrapt attention, whereas if I even stir my lips for the same purpose they become impatient to tell me to shut up.

The majority of painters, English and Irish, are poorly educated, but they have an amazing knowledge of racing and football; their chief conversation, day after day, being about these subjects. They know the history of each horse and player as well as if they lived next door. They have a set of "dead certs" before each race, and if they had half the faith in God that they have in horses, they would have no need to worry about eternity. Each expects for sure to make his fortune out of betting on the races.

One of them worked with me on a job, and his most memorable characteristic was a set of overalls which had so much paint and dirt on them that it seemed quite impossible to get them cleaned by any means. He looked reckless in general, which was rather unusual for an Englishman. He was by no means impudent, but he kept telling me how clever he was for picking winners in all the big races.

If that is the case, said I in my own mind, isn't it surprising he does not get himself a new set of overalls!

"I have a system," he said, "and it works every time. I have a system, you see."

"Why do you come to work at all if you can make such a success of your system?" I asked.

"Bli' me, I can't put it into operation," he said, "because I'm short of money."

"For pity's sake!" said I, a little sarcastically, having no doubts about what he said.

"I'll tell you what I'll do," said he, hopefully. "If you lend me twenty pounds I'll guarantee to make it worth your while and you'll never regret it."

"What would you do with it if I gave it to you?" I asked out of curiosity.

"I have a system, you see," he explained. "Give me the twenty pounds and you'll soon find out. I'll bring you back double the money next Monday."

He kept on urging me to give him the money, always reminding me that he had a system until finally I lost my temper.

"If you have a system, my dear man," said I, looking in disdain at his grimy overalls, "go away and apply it to yourself! You need it more than I do."

If I did not agree with the political views of particular Irishmen I was in trouble also. They told me with great emphasis which was the best party for ruling Ireland. It was always their own. I needed enlightenment in that respect, so they started to teach me at once, even though a child of seven would feel ashamed of the way they pronounced some of their words. Once when one of them wanted to humiliate me in front of others, by showing how far advanced he was over me by reason of the fact that he was doing a course with a Correspondence College in Oxford, I quietly brought him to earth by a few curt sentences in my own defence. But it was no use; he still went on blowing, after expressing annoyance at my cheek to interrupt him at all. "You couldn't lurn me nottin', mate," he told me, in the supreme glory of his own great adventures in the sea of knowledge. It will be seen from his mode of expression that I was not likely to have attempted any such feat as trying to enlighten him in any way.

When I came to England first, if anyone said a word against Churchill, he would run the risk of being assassinated by the working classes. But now that the war was over, they had changed their minds! They were all in favour of the Labour Party, and because Churchill was a Tory they despised him as a result. If there was a rise in wages, they said the Labour Party was responsible for it. Both English and Irish workers gave this party credit for everything good that happened, while the Tories were always blamed if anything went wrong. When the National Insurance Service came into operation there was no mention of Sir William Beveridge who first planned it. The Labour Party got all the credit. Sir William was even rejected by the voters when he stood for parliament. How could he succeed when these blinded ignorant fanatics seemed to think that the very shining of the sun came through the goodness of the Labour Party!

I enjoyed the privilege of being able to go from job to job when I liked, and often said it was a fine thing compared with the time before the war when men had to cling for bare life to whatever work they had, no matter what the snags were, because if they left, they could find nothing else to do.

"It's a jolly fine thing, surely," my companions would say, "and we may thank the Labour Party for that."

Being so sick listening to the same thing over and over again, I would lose my temper and burst out in a storm:

"My dear friends," I would say, for I had no politics, "we owe these conditions to neither Labour, Liberal nor Conservative."

"Who do we owe them to then?" they would flare back at me, feeling that there was a traitor in the camp, and a cheeky one at that.

"We owe them to an Austrian called Adolf Hitler!" I would retort.

"Who?" they would ask.

"Hitler!" I would assure them. "He did a lot of harm in his time, the Lord save us, but he did a lot of good as well. None of your great politicians could settle the unemployment question in the hungry thirties, for all their talk and promises of wonders that might happen if people went to polling booths in rags, and voted in their favour, so as to send them into parliament to fight and get them bread. No; not even Ramsay MacDonald could do that. Nobody could, indeed; but Hitler did!"

The monotony of their talk gave me the impression that their vocabulary was limited in spite of boasted knowledge;

as a working class so different from the Irish peasantry, both men and women, who could brighten up a mortuary itself by twisting language on a swivel of the brain-box, generating wit and humour like a laughing magazine.

When I told them of my liking for a change in work they laughed and said my method would most likely send me hungry to the workhouse. Most of them would rather stay with one employer, no matter how awkward he was, rather than move from place to place. Some were forty years with the same firm and I did not envy them because I learned more by wandering.

Quite a lot had very high opinions of their skill as painters and boasted of the many firms that had asked them back after they had left for some reason or another.

"Why then, I have worked for fifty-seven since I came to England," I would say, in contrast to the bursting of their glory, "and damn the one of them ever asked for my return!"

So I too had a record, and managed to live happily in spite of it, by the grace of God, without having either to beg, borrow or steal!

I must mention here however about one glorious exception I met in the line of intelligence and education. He was a tall, lively, cheerful young man, and though he did not wear white overalls, I noticed that he got on with his work very fast and well. I first met him in a big warehouse at Camden Town. I took no particular notice of him until one day as I spoke to my companions quite casually about something, he stopped working and looked at me.

"You talk like someone out of the fourteenth century," said he for a start, and I took that as a compliment when I thought of the terrible slang I heard around me in the twentieth! "Where do you come from?"

"County Kerry, Ireland," said I. "Everyone talks there as I do."

We became friends from that out and I found him a man of extraordinary intellectual powers. He was self-educated and was after reading most of the world's best literature, so with my usual flare for information, I began to ask about his life. He was married he said to a Canadian girl and they had five children. I could hardly believe it, because he did not wear the worried look I always notice on the faces of men as soon as ever they get wives! He was as jolly a man as any I had ever met in Ireland. His name was Albert Seymour.

Before many days had passed he invited me to his home for tea, which was an honour only one other painter had ever given me before, though I had worked with many in my time. I met his family at the house and found them very nicely-mannered. His wife was cheerful too. She had fair hair, fresh complexion, humorous ways and a hearty laugh. I enjoyed the tea to perfection, for she had an art in making it which few women possess. I could nearly swear that if I was deaf, dumb and blind, I could easily recognise her tea by taste alone.

Some time after this the Firm sent each of us to different jobs, but after about three weeks we met again at a college in South Kensington. I had been there only a few hours however when the sorrowful news came that my friend was after falling from some very high scaffolding and was not expected to live. I went at once to see him lying on the ground and barely able to whisper. Though the weather was very warm at the time, his face was cold to the touch and I was afraid his end was near. We got him to hospital and then Ernie, the Foreman, a very kind and considerate fellow, arranged for me to go to Brixton and tell my friend's wife about the trouble. I went at once by bus and tried to keep a cheerful face so as not to alarm her. She began to prepare tea, and I left her do so; then quietly told her aunt who was with her, to break the news as gently as possible, so that I could take them both to the hospital.

Albert was in bed when we arrived, and though quite cheerful, was kept on the danger list for four days. After that he was put in a plaster jacket and kept in hospital for three months. Then he came home, still wearing the jacket but never grumbling, apart from saying he was very annoyed at times when his back itched under the plaster.

He got over that trouble however by pushing a long knitting needle underneath to get at the itchy part!

"It is like love," he said with a laugh; "an itch where you cannot scratch!"

WHILST living at Onslow Square I got lots of work in offices and showrooms around the West End of London, and as I found my English companions very helpful, I soon got on well at the trade, so that in the end I was not afraid of being sent anywhere to work, provided there was no racing to be done, because I was too slow with the brush to keep the pace where that was concerned.

Some of the offices were extremely dirty, but when we had cleaned them out and painted them neatly, nobody came along and said "That looks better"; but if we made a mistake such as missing a little patch, the critics' eyes would focus on it like a magnet-needle pointing to the pole, the minute they entered the room, and they would draw our attention to it at once. If they had no fault to find with the painting, they usually walked about, completely ignoring the presence of the painter as they talked with the supervisor who usually came with them, pointing to this corner and that. The gist of their conversation was usually: "Heah," as they pointed to a corner where they wanted a certain article of furniture placed, and "heah, and heah," again as they pointed to other corners with such sombre seriousness that one might think the placing of these articles anywhere else might disturb the changeless fixing of the heavenly constellations. I never heard them say anything bright or witty except on one occasion when a well-known lady came to see her new house. "I know nothing about that," she said frankly, "but like all politicians, I can talk!"

Sometimes when the owner of a dirty house found fault after we had cleaned and painted a room, I lost my temper and told her in the words of Doctor Johnson that, like Goldsmith, we "touched nothing we did not adorn!"

As a rule, before any complaints were made, the builders sent a supervisor on the job to see that all was well. Some of these were very strict on the men and were disliked as a result.

After a painter had distempered a ceiling, the story goes, a labourer told him he had accidentally touched it with the end of a ladder, making a mark that looked like a miss. The painter was on the scaffold doing another ceiling when the supervisor came fuming into the room.

"Have you seen that miss in the last ceiling you did?" he asked.

"That wasn't a miss, Sir," said the painter.

"It was a miss," said the supervisor.

"It wasn't, Sir," said the painter, going on to tell about the ladder, but being interrupted by the supervisor who persisted in his argument that it was.

The painter dipped his brush into the bucket of distemper, waited till the supervisor turned his eyes to the ground, then dashed it all over him, calling out with bitter sarcasm at the same time: "That wasn't a miss, was it!"

After a few years in the trade I felt that my health had gone down a lot and I began to think that perhaps the paint was the cause of it; but before I had time to do anything about it, we all got notice to leave the hostel, so I decided on visiting my old landladies at Swanley to ask if they could take me in again. I was in luck, for they gave me a great welcome, so I went back to live there and was delighted with the nicely-cooked food as well as many other conveniences which could not be had in the hostel.

There was another pleasant surprise in store for me too, because I had been only about a month in Swanley when my health began to improve, thank God, and I became a new man. Then I understood why I was feeling so run down in London. The air there disagreed with me; so I saw once more the truth of the Royal Commission's finding that Swanley was the healthiest inland place in England.

During all this time of course I had never forgotten Ireland, so when June came I decided on paying it a visit. First of all I applied to the Emigration Authorities to change the word "Labourer" on my travel permit to that of "Painter." They did so, and I was delighted to think I had got on so well in the building trade, in spite of the fact that I never liked it, except as a help to get me bread.

I took a bath the day before leaving and wore my new

navy-blue suit for the journey. In the boat going across the Irish sea I met a grand-daughter to White River Denny from Gurthagreenane who was on her way home from Chatham Hospital where she was employed as a nurse. I was delighted to see her, and thought of her mother's lovely singing long ago. As we got near the shores of Ireland and the Harbour of O'Leary's Dhoon, my heart rose with joy at the idea of landing there again, saying to myself, "I love the graceful sea-gulls that fly over Dublin Bay," as I saw them glide smoothly through the air above the boat.

All went well until we were about to cross the barrier on to the platform from which we were to take the train to Dublin. White River Denny's grand-daughter stepped across after showing her travel permit. But when I showed mine, and the official saw the word "Painter" on it, he beckoned to his companion, who said to me: "This way, please."

I was wondering what was up, even though I expected many things in those days, but I soon found out. He was taking me to the fumigation chamber so that if I had any English bugs on me they might be made harmless! Before being allowed to enter Holy Old Ireland I had to be clean, of course, and no doubt I looked scruffy after the tiresome journey, so my judges were not going to take any chances. I felt like Moses when the Lord said: "Take off thy boots, for the ground wherein thou standest is holy!" because these emigration officials made me dip my boots into a dish of disinfectant. After that they put me standing in a narrow cupboard like a coffin with nothing but my head stuck out! It was like being put in the stocks of long ago. They puffed a noxious gas all over my body till they thought the vermin were stifled. I was nearly stifled too; stifled and humiliated. The Irish again, said I in my own mind; always ready to despise their own race whenever they get a chance! If I were a big politician, nobody would dare to have me fumigated at the Harbour of O'Leary's Dhoon, but because I was a mere painter, they did not have to worry, for they felt that I had no redress. Workers must always take back seats in Ireland and be subjected to humiliations by worthless officials while politicians are occupying front ones and getting all the honours on their way back from world conferences after giving advice to men of other countries instead of staying at home to put their own house in order. Just like their brothers telling me what I should do in painting. I survived it all however and got out in time to help my neighbour to find a place to stay for the night before going on to Kerry.

After I had spent a few days with my brothers in Dublin I went by train to Gurthagreenane where I met my old friends and from there to my sister's place outside Kenmare.

On my return to England there was no personal fumigation at Holyhead as there had been in the Irish harbour. Workers get the same treatment at that Welsh port as anyone else. Only in Ireland is class distinction brought to the pitch of a fine art.

After returning to Swanley I found a job painting a kitchen at Pall Mall in London. My companion was an Englishman; a very decent fellow but a rank Communist. In spite of that however we got on well together, because each made allowances for the different views of the other. He regarded Communism as a means of turning this world into paradise. He preached his theory whenever he got the chance, but in a different way to that in which my Irish political companions tried to stress theirs, making sure that their opponents had no chance to talk at all. I had a very high regard for him in that respect, and we remained friends all the time we were together.

One day a labourer came in and told us he was leaving to go on a job with another firm nearby where he was to get extra money for the same work.

"Painters are getting sixpence an hour over the rate there as well," he whispered, for fear the Foreman might hear him.

That put us thinking, so during the dinner hour my Communist friend and I went to find out if it was true. We soon reached the site at the end of a little street called Cleveland Row. It was a vast building called Bridgewater House. My mind was greatly elevated when I went in to what was called The Great Hall which had noble pillars all around it holding up galleries covered with beautifully-painted, dome-shaped canopies.

This is the place for me, said I in my own mind, as I stared about me in wonder and delight.

"Where is the paint-shop, mate?" I heard my companion ask a workman who was eating his lunch as he sat with his back against one of the pillars.

"Down in the basement," he answered. "Go through that door," he added, pointing to the right, "then along the corridor till you see the stairs at the end. When you get down anyone will tell you where the paint-shop is. You can't go wrong."

I thought of the Englishman's "round the coaneh," and the Irishman's "mile and a bit," as we struggled through a mazes of arches, doors and corridors until we found the paint-shop at last.

Some of the painters were sitting on distemper drums and other vessels, having their lunch as we went in, for many like them never care for fresh air.

"Is the Foreman about?" asked my companion.

"Right here, old boy," said a low-sized ginger-haired man in white. "What can I do for you?"

"Does your Firm pay sixpence an hour over the rate?"

"Yes. Do you want a job?"

"Both of us do."

"When can you start?"

"To-morrow, if that suits you."

"Very well then. Bring your tools here at eight in the morning."

It was Friday, and according to the rules of the trade we were entitled to leave the old Firm by giving the Foreman two hours' notice, so we went back and told him we were leaving. He was upset, but we could not help that, so we finished with him that evening.

We started to work at Bridgewater House on the following morning and it did me good to look around whenever I lifted my eyes from the job I was doing. It was a glorious building inside, and it made me think of the song: "I dreamt I dwelt in marble halls."

Our Firm had about thirty painters working there, and we all sat around long tables for tea, morning and evening. It was a strict Union Firm and we had to show our cards to the shop steward before we were very long on the job.

Soon my Communist friend began trying to make converts

to his cause, and became very popular because of his talk of being all out to serve the workers. One day he suggested a collection of sixpence a man for some Communist purpose. Each gave his money as the hat was passed along until it came to me. I kept my arms folded and made no move to give anything. The man with the hat waited; wondering no doubt at the cheek of anyone daring to be different in a case like that. All the men looked at me too.

"Come on, Paddy," said the tall loud-spoken Scotsman who was Shop Steward, and therefore a man of great power, " 'tis only sixpence."

"Jock," said I, looking him straight in the face, "if you want to hear it, I know the value of a sixpence as well as you do, but I know the value of a principle as well."

"Principle be damned," he said with a sneer. "You're afraid o' th' old Pope, that's what it is."

"I'm afraid of neither Pope nor Prelate," said I with emphasis; "for they have never done anything to make me so. I'm a Roman Catholic, and I'm not going to support any cause which is opposed to my Faith. The man who suggested the collection is my friend. He knows well enough that I have no grudge against him personally."

"I know that perfectly well, Brian," said the Communist, like the gentleman he was.

When the Scotsman started off again, a fellow Irishman spoke up on my behalf, saying I was right to stand by my principles; and when it was all over, many of the others who were afraid to say anything at the time, came along and privately congratulated me on what I was after doing. I had kept my honour as I thought proper and I still had my Communist friend into the bargain. I liked him, because I always admire a straight man no matter what his beliefs may be.

Every six weeks the Firm paid a supplementary bonus as well as the sixpence an hour extra, so that it was a good job for money, but after I had been there a month I heard a rumour that some of the painters were to be sacked. A talkative charge-hand was overheard saying in a nearby public house that I would be among the first to go, because I was not working fast enough, so one of my friends brought me the news in the quiet, and I was prepared.

"This is a big surprise to me, Paddy," said the same charge-hand as he came to me a week later with my notice.

"'Tis no surprise to me, Jim," said I with a touch of sarcasm. "I knew it a week ago!"

The Communist was sacked with me and we both went off together as friendly as ever. I was surprised in his case because he was a fast worker. It was a curious thing that if a man was sacked on this particular job, he became entitled to the supplementary bonus, but if he left of his own accord he lost his right to it! I knew this, so after I had been away for a few weeks I went back to the Firm to claim it and was paid promptly. When I had the money in my pocket I took a walk about the building which I never grew tired of admiring, and as there was another firm doing a much more delicate sort of painting there, I went to its Foreman and asked for a job. He gave it to me, and to the great surprise of my previous Foreman and charge-hand I was back at work again, completely independent of them, in the same house!

The Communist was working nearby, so when I met him by accident one day, I asked him did he get his bonus.

"What bonus?" he asked in surprise, for apparently he had been so deeply interested in the spread of propaganda that he never had time to think about it. This was most unusual, for every man of his creed that I ever met was always out for the highest money; so much so in fact that I could not help concluding that every Communist is a Capitalist at heart.

"The supplementary bonus," I told him. "Three guineas and three pennies—the same as I got. Come back with me to Bridgewater House and ask for it."

He did and got it without any trouble.

I had to laugh at the principle on which this money was paid, but I had already learned that the sack was often a blessing in disguise in more ways than one. I heard of an Irishman who wanted to leave a bad job during the war and would not be allowed to do so. He did everything possible to deserve getting the sack, but always failed. One day the General Foreman sent him across the site for a wheelbarrow, and after staying away for a very unreasonable time, he returned with two, one inside in the other.

"I told you where to find that wheelbarrow," said the

General in a rage, "and why didn't you bring it back at once?"

"Well now Sir, indeed," said Paddy, "between you and me and the mixer, 'twas an awkward thing to bring for a lone man."

"You were an awkward man to send for it too," said the General; "and who the hell told you to bring two of them?"

"You didn't expect me to bring the first one on my back, did you?" asked the Irishman, still hoping to get his cards and failing even then!

He was on the point of despair in the end when it came to him all of a sudden. He nearly died of joy. Seeing his cards in his hands at last, he could hardly believe his eyes or his good luck as he walked dramatically to and fro before the man who graced him with the sack so long desired!

"I'm grateful," he said, striking his breast, "deeply grateful!" Then jerking his head into the air, and flinging out his hands in token of the flowing thanks that filled his heart, he added: "In fact, I'm not only grateful; I'm profoundly honoured!"

After spending a few months with the second Firm at Bridgewater House I was out of work again by the beginning of December, and as I knew from experience that it was next to impossible to get a painting job between then and Easter, I became a temporary postman delivering Christmas mails at Bexley Heath. I found this job most interesting. In the early hours of the morning I cycled to the sorting office, sat at a desk and picked out the letters for my round which was on a long road called Rydal Drive. Before leaving the office, I was taught to put the letters in rotation corresponding to the numbers of the houses where they were to be delivered, tying with a piece of string those for each particular section of my round, so that letters for Number Three, Seven and Twelve appeared one after the other on top of each bundle as I went along. This method took a lot of time at the office but it made up for it later on by preventing confusion on the route.

The Post Office people were far superior to those in the building trade, and the dear knows that was easy for them. They used no filthy language and were very nice to work with. There was a comfortable canteen in the office where we had our meals before going out, and again when we returned.

On the road the real trouble began. Everything went well until I came to a house with a registered letter for which the Post Office wanted a receipt. No reply at the front door, nor to a bang on the back window either, so I would have to put the letter back into my pocket and try again on my return journey.

Some greeting cards were so big that they would not go through the letter-box openings, and the sender from complete lack of thought for the postman, would have written "Please do not bend" on the envelope. Again no answer at the door, so I would go around to the back in a wild hurry to see if any window was left open by chance so that I might drop the card through it instead. All windows shut, so I would have to hold on to that big awkward "unbendable" card which had been chosen, no doubt, by its sender, to create an impression by size alone! Once I decided on leaving such a card outside the front door but if I did, the owner of the house returned soon after, watched out for me on the way back and told me curtly that leaving a card like that was not a proper delivery.

"Agreed, Sir," said I with equal curtness, urged on by an Irish temper, for I was late at the time. "If I have anything for you to-morrow and the doors are shut, I'll take it back to the sorting office and leave it there till the rush is over. I've got a lot more letters and parcels to deliver along this road, bad cess to it, and I can't spare time to sit like Lazarus on your doorstep, looking up into the bosom of the mighty Abraham till perhaps the thought of dinner gives you pleasure to return."

He was neither bad nor ignorant, so he saw my point at once. He called after me as I was opening the gate leading to the street.

"I must apologise," he said at once. "Lack of understanding your position made me rude enough to lose my temper, and I'm sorry. Use your own discretion with my letters in future. You know how to respect the valuable ones."

"Yes, Sir," I said, "and I also know how to respect a

gentleman with courage and manners enough to apologise; for I can assure you that it is rarely I get the chance of doing so."

We shook hands before parting, and after that I felt I would gladly have taken a day off to see that his mail was properly delivered, and he seemed to know it.

When I came with registered parcels I was always greeted with a pleasant smile everywhere and given the required receipts, but with one honourable exception where a woman gave me a money present, nobody ever said "Would you like a cup of tea?" till I came to a bungalow called "Wynberg" where a nice pleasant-faced young woman called Rosa from the Yorkshire Dales was married to a man called Tom Tremain. She invited me into the house, gave me a glass of wine and a money present, after introducing me to her husband and mother. I found them all very nice people whom it was a pleasure to know. They told me to come back for tea later on. They are still my friends and I have paid them many visits since then. This family and one other are the only two I can remember with gratitude among the three or four hundred houses at which I delivered letters and parcels. Mind you, I was neither hungry nor thirsty on the way, but I always like sociable gestures and feel bad when they are missing.

From this adventure with the Post Office I learned to be for ever after sympathetic to postmen. It was borne in upon me on account of having to rush from house to house with a heavy load of mails on my back; meeting a cross dog here; a locked door next; a small opening in a letter-box after that; as well as being forced to jump over walls and barbed wire from one garden into another, rushing to deliver my burden so that I might get home as soon as possible and have a short sleep.

In late spring when the weather got fine I returned to painting in London and as I worked and watched, I thought of the wonderful way in which big blocks of offices were put up, for, like the making of a railway, this never struck my mind until I found myself actually in the business. Labourers dug foundations and laid the concrete base; steel-erectors put up the iron framework; bricklayers built the walls; carpenters did the woodwork; plasterers faced the walls; plumbers fitted in the baths and lavatory pans; electricians put in the lighting system; and finally the painters put a finish to it all.

In the beginning of autumn I had the good luck of being sent to work with a firm engaged in renovating Lancaster House near Buckingham Palace. There was a vast and very beautiful hall in this building also, and it is said that when Queen Victoria paid a neighbourly visit to it long ago she said to the owner, the Duchess of Sutherland: "I have left my house to visit your palace!" It was certainly worthy of the honour. A great lantern like that on the Octagon of Ely let in the light from a mighty height above the hall. Giant figures in human shape seemed to hold it on their backs, and between them were clumps of big shining golden leek-like plants. The beautifully-decorated ceilings in other parts of the building were a sight to see, as well as the magnificent doors and windows which were adorned with intricate mouldings painted in light cream and gold. I certainly felt proud of the honour of being a painter in such a place. It was a far cry from the days when I first tried to get into the trade. I now felt qualified to work in any sort of building, though knowing perfectly well that I was still only a learner; a fact that all honourable tradesmen will readily admit up to the day they retire of old age. Only the ignorant will say "I know all about it. There is nothing in painting." Any fool can certainly put paint on a wall. Putting it on correctly so that it will not run into heaps is another matter, like the proper mixing of colours.

About fifty painters were employed on this job when I came there. The majority were casuals who were given a promise of six months' work, and I was amongst these. But we soon found that the Firm had a lot of "blue-eyes" attached to it. Among them was the Shop Steward, a rather decent fellow, though somewhat clever, like Mike from Cahermore, where his own benefit was concerned. I noticed that whenever any of the Union Organisers came on the job, they always had a pleasant talk with him, but there was never any change for the better in working conditions after he had left.

All went well for about two months and the Foreman treated us fairly, though the work was often very monotonous.

We had a visit now and again from the Supervisor. He walked about the job with a serious mask-like face so that I could not help laughing to myself and regarding him as "The Knight of the Rueful Countenance!" He had wit and humour at the back of it all, I found out later, for my friend, Albert Seymour, who had previously worked for the Firm, told me about him. Once he arrived on a job where a lot of statues had to be covered with sheets before painters could begin to work. When this was done, the men sat down to smoke, and he saw them. Standing on a balcony above them with the Foreman, he turned to him and asked: "Have you covered all these figures?"

"I have," said the Foreman, wondering why he asked such a simple question.

"You have not," said the Supervisor with a severe look.

"I'm sure I have, Sir," said the Foreman, more perplexed than ever.

"You haven't covered these, have you?" asked the Supervisor, pointing down at the smoking painters, still sitting and puffing away to their hearts' content!

When most of the washing-down was done by the casuals, the regulars began to trickle into the job by threes and fours, week after week. Rumours then went out that some of the casuals were to be sacked, so that the "blue-eyes" might remain. On principle that was unfair, for the casuals had been promised six months' employment, and apart from that, nobody liked the idea of doing all the dirty work so that another might come along and do the painting after him. While these rumours were going around I was given into charge of a new Foreman who had come from one of the outside jobs, and that was the beginning of trouble for me, for he was badly-disposed towards me from the start. I could please him in nothing, though I had pleased the other Foreman in everything. He was the most prejudiced man I had met in charge of any job since I came to England. The painters were afraid to say a word against him, even behind his back, in case it reached his ears, while I had often seen many of the same type of men make no denial of their hatred for a decent Foreman. He made my life a misery on the job. He disregarded Union Rules whenever it suited him and nobody had the courage to complain. This went on for weeks and when I could bear it no longer I told the London Union Office what was happening in a typewritten letter, explaining that I dare not give my name for fear of reprisals. Nobody on the job knew what I had done as I waited quietly for the result.

On the third day after posting, an Irish labourer who tended the painters came along my way full of excitement saying that things were humming all over the place because someone had made a terrible complaint to the Union. Buckets of water were lined along the wall for the men to wash, he said; towels and soap were provided, as well as many other facilities which the Firm did not even bother thinking about before. An Organiser was coming on the job, and all the men were to be assembled in the dining-room when he arrived.

I was excited of course and delighted to think that my letter was after making such a stir in the place for the good of the workers, but I dare not show a sign of it to anyone because I knew I would get little thanks but plenty blame for doing it even from those who might get most benefit from it, for I knew their nature.

When the meeting started, the Organiser, whom I had never seen before, got on a bench and addressed the crowd, explaining about the letter and the subject of the complaint.

"Why wasn't the person who wrote that letter man enough to sign his name to it?" asked the big hefty grey-haired long-service paint-shop colour-man, who was keeping a watching brief for the Firm in an unofficial capacity.

"I can understand perfectly well why he did not do so," said the Organiser, whose name was Albert Silverstein, "and every other common-sense painter understands it as well. He fears reprisals from the Firm, and is quite right in acting as he did. I would very much like to meet him, and if he is listening to me now, I hope he will make himself known by some means or other."

I was standing a few feet away from him at the time but I was careful not to blink an eyelid, knowing that from the poor opinion painters in general had of my abilities, none of them would expect that I could type.

He went on to criticise the actions of the Firm, as well as the neglect of the Shop Steward in not having the cause of the complaint attended to himself, for I had stated clearly in my letter that this man, as a "blue-eye," had been appointed to his post before the majority of the men had come to work at Lancaster House, which was an action I thought might prejudice the interests of the casuals as a result. I admired the independent way in which this Organiser did his job without fear of either Firm or Shop Steward, for he kept both in their places with very direct language.

The Shop Steward, who was used to having it all his own way up to now with the other Organisers, began to throw the blame on the nameless man who made the complaint, so as to save himself.

"People who do things like that," he said, "are not trade unionists, but individualists," forgetting that when unions try to suppress individuals they only succeed in making rebels.

He got nowhere with his argument, for Silverstein was a fine fellow with an open mind who was out for the good of painters in general, and who proved himself right worthy of the trust they had in him.

When he was gone, there was a very marked improvement in everything, and you may be sure the Firm took good care to see that it continued.

About a month after this a report went out that twenty of the casuals were to be sacked. There was a strong suspicion that this was being done so that the Firm's favourites might not have to go instead. Everyone was upset about it, as the time was close to Christmas, and the likelihood of getting another job remote. Soon the day came and the Foreman gave me notice with the usual "Sorry, Pat; you know the way things are." I did, and so did the nineteen others who were to go with me. Nobody knew what to do, so we all dressed up and got ready to leave as soon as we got our money and cards. Then someone got a brain-wave. He went out and telephoned the Union Office. Down came Silverstein at once; the right man in the right place at the right time. He had but two hours in which to work, but Silverstein was no ordinary Organiser, and he proved it that evening. He got in touch with the Firm's Office and threatened a strike at once if the Management insisted on getting rid of the men. In all fairness to the "blue-eyes," they stood by us in our trouble and promised to support the strike if it started. But Silverstein won a victory for us, and through his good services we were kept at work by the Firm for another month.

Then when everything had settled down, I wrote and told him who I was, thanking him for attending so promptly to my letter, and for the excellent work he was after doing for all of us.

XXIII *ACTING THE SANCHO PANZA*

DURING all these years, the different Firms I worked for kept an average of about thirty shillings a week from my wages for income tax and national insurance before ever they handed me my pay packets, so that there was no means left by which I could escape payment. I never got any personal return for this money except when I was unemployed, got sick or went to hospital. Then it was very nice to get free treatment and sickness benefit as well. When I was out of work the Labour Exchange people regarded the money they paid me more as a gift on their part than as a right on mine, and never liked the idea of paying it if they could avoid doing so. I resented this attitude when I thought of the number of careless drunken lazy men who made wrecks of their lives and then drew national assistance money because they were destitute through their own fault. My contribution in taxes was there to help them, but to the Labour Exchange people, it was demanding too much when I expected some of it to help myself.

One year I got the sack early in December when work usually began to get slack. It was very cold at the time, with a bitter wind blowing leaves, papers and straws along the roads and laneways. I had registered for work at the local

Labour Exchange, and in the course of a few days the postman brought me a letter containing an introduction card from the Manager to a Firm building council houses at a place called Sutton-at-Hone, near Swanley. I never liked that sort of work since I did it with another Irishman some years previously at Headstone Lane, near Harrow-on-the-Hill. We were earning bonus, and as the houses were being put up in a hurry for the working classes, the Firm did not seem to worry much about the way the painting was done. They knew well that the tenants were only too glad to get into them, and would not bother about complaining, so they sent a man with a spraying machine, dragging his fittings after him like a frightened donkey with a bunch of tin cans tied to his tail by mischievous little boys, to spray the walls with amazing quickness, putting on the shower of paint at random, thick in one place, thin in another, because he could not spare time to do the job properly. When he had left, our job was to paint the woodwork and any of the awkward corners which he could not reach. I never saw such racing in all my life, and of course I could not carry on with it, so I left the job before the week was out. I regarded the rushing as a clever trick on the part of the Firm to get two days' work for one day's pay by dangling a few extra shillings in the shape of bonus before the eyes of ignorant painters who could not see that they were being exploited.

Considering the time of the year however and knowing that jobs were scarce, I decided on taking a chance at Sutton-at-Hone, for I never liked being out of work at Christmas if I could help it, so I handed in my cards to the Firm and made a start.

The Foreman took me along a slippery path leading from the office to the public road through a rough gap in a thorny hedge, then over heaps of freshly turned earth, made sticky by recent rain and snow, to the house I was to paint. He handed me my kit in a wild hurry and showed me what to do, standing by to watch me. I started to paint a door first, and as there was a biting breeze getting at me through an open window, I went across to shut it. He looked at me in blank amazement. What I did seemed waste of precious time in his eyes, it seemed. He went off then, but during my first three hours at work he visited me seven times to see that I kept moving. I did, and finished my movements by crossing the swamp to the office and asking for my cards. The Foreman was in no way surprised, for I expect I was not the first to leave that job in a hurry.

"I haven't your money now," he said, "but if you come back in the morning you'll get it."

"Thank you," said I, going across the mud again, taking off my overalls and leaving.

On the following day after getting my money I went back to the Labour Exchange and applied for unemployment benefit, saying the job at Sutton-at-Hone was not suitable.

In the course of a few days the Manager sent me a notice stating that because I had left my job without reasonable cause my payment would be suspended for six weeks on the instructions of the National Insurance Officer. I could, if I wished, appeal against this before the Local Tribunal set up by the Ministry.

I was flaring, and small wonder, indeed. So that was the blinking government's method of punishing me for refusing to keep my nose to the grindstone! If that was the idea then, we were well on our way towards the slave state. They might get me to work willingly, but they were not going to force me by any means if I could stop it. I thought of the old Irish-woman in the song who said to her son: "Heaven forbid I'd ever be the mother of a slave!" Mine was not to be the mother of one either. Yes; I would certainly apply for redress to the Tribunal, even if it was only to show up the methods of the people in office.

I reviewed the position carefully. Here was I, deprived of my just rights by somebody called the National Insurance Officer acting as dictator and deciding that I should have stayed in an unpleasant job whether I liked it or not. The spirit of the Irish was overlooked when that decision was made.

The Ministry of National Insurance sent me a form on which to write my reasons for leaving. I put them all down frankly and sent it back.

Then I prepared my case, writing down a set of questions

I intended to ask the National Insurance Officer if the Chairman of the Tribunal allowed me to do so.

The Painters' Union sent a man to help me. I met him outside the office in which the Tribunal was to sit, but when I introduced myself, he became suddenly conceited, flared up and told me I was a nuisance bringing a busy man like him on a fool's errand in such a case when it was a foregone conclusion that it was lost.

"My goodness, man," said I, dumbfounded, "I didn't ask you to come down."

"You haven't the ghost of a chance," he said, "and I don't like wasting time on a silly case like this."

"You're very pessimistic," said I, thinking how different he was to Silverstein, who always seemed to have a hopeful outlook.

"The statement you made on your form is all against you anyhow," he said. "You played into their hands by telling them why you left. I hadn't much time for studying it, but I could see at a glance that it was foolish."

"It was a frank statement," said I, "and I can stand by every word of it," adding in my own mind that before night came down the wind might leave his sails.

When I saw his astonishing attitude I became all the more determined to fight the case alone and be completely independent of him should he decline to help me. My method was to act the Sancho Panza, get at the humorous side of the Chairman if he had any; then play my cards to the best advantage while he smiled, for I knew he would be human as well as the rest of us.

When the time came, I was brought in and put sitting at a table beside the Union Official, right in front of the Chairman. He had a very serious look on him and so had everyone else.

My case was read and the Union Official asked if he had any defence to make on my behalf.

"Yes, Sir," he said, addressing the Chairman. "We have had trouble with the Firm he left about other things as well," and he went on to say as best he could that I had a good right to leave them.

I kept very quiet and said nothing until all the others were finished.

"Well," said the Chairman to me at last, "have you anything to say for yourself?"

"Oh yes, Sir," said I, "if you're kind enough to let me talk, and if my brogue does not upset the carriage of my speech, I have lots of things to say."

"Go on then," he said, "say them."

"May I see the National Insurance Officer first?" I asked, drawing the sheet of questions from my pocket; and I noticed eyebrows lifting all around me, as might happen if a tramp took out a notebook and asked a policeman for his name. "I want to ask him a few questions."

"Get the National Insurance Officer," said the Chairman to the Clerk; and then turning to me he added: "Perhaps it might be better for you to tell me what you want to say and I can ask the questions myself."

"The pleasure is mine to do as you say, Sir," said I, examining my papers with the air of a crusted Old Bailey attorney. "In the first place, the summons which called me here says I should not attend if I am out of the district. How in the name of goodness could I attend if I was out of the district?"

A broad smile came over the face of the Chairman. Then I knew I was getting somewhere. I heard a muffled giggle in the room also which gave me encouragement to rest on my oars.

"Go on," said the Chairman, either pleased or taken off his guard. "We're in a hurry."

As he spoke, a well-dressed woman with reddish hair came in and sat among the others. A bad sign, said I in my own mind, but it was too late now for me to turn back!

"The National Insurance Officer says in his statement that I did not stay long enough in the job to give it a fair trial," I went on, "because I only stayed three and a half hours in it. Will you kindly ask him when he comes in, how long he will stay in a puddle himself if he steps into one without his Wellington boots?"

There was another laugh all over the room. I found out later that the National Insurance Officer was not a man at all, but the red-haired woman who had just come in!

197

"He doesn't stay in it for three and a half hours, I'm telling you, or for three and a half minutes either," I continued, to the amazement and apparent delight of all present, except perhaps the female concerned. "No," said I with force of words, "because as an intelligent man, he sees the folly at once of staying in it too long. Even a donkey with a sack drawn over his eyes would know that. But me! Look at me, everybody! I'm supposed to stay in it because I'm only a simple working biped with no sense in me at all. Am I a man or a cog in a wheel? I hope everybody will see if the sack is off their eyes, that the National Insurance Officer's argument is narrow and groundless. With the spirit of Christmas in the air, I hope the Tribunal will see its way to cancel the suspension of benefit which this Officer is after putting on me."

"Thank you," said the Chairman with his hand over his mouth. "That will do."

As I rose to go I wished him the compliments of the season, for after all it was no murder trial!

He turned to me and smiled again.

"What part of Ireland do you come from?" he asked in a very sociable way as if he had known me for quite a while.

"County Kerry, Sir," said I, going outside to wait for his decision and feeling at the same time that the case was won.

I was right, because in a short time the Union Official came running up to me and tapped me on the shoulder.

"Touch wood," he said, smiling pleasantly. "You're a lucky man. I've been fourteen years in this job and I never before saw a painter win a case like that."

"Did you ever hear what Daniel O'Connell said long ago?" I asked.

"No," said he. "What was it?"

"That an Irishman could drive a coach and four through every Act of Parliament the English ever made!"

"You seem to have done something like that now," he said, handing me a green slip of paper stating: "In the matter considered to-day the Tribunal gave a decision in your favour," and signed by the Chairman.

Expecting to be out of work for a few months during the slack time in the painting business, I decided on trying my hand at something else if I could find a suitable job. Hearing that a helper was wanted in a fruit-pulping station at Swanley I went there to ask about it. I was received kindly at the office.

"Do you want a helper, Sir?" I asked the Manager, a broad-shouldered pleasant-faced man.

"Yes," he said. "We do."

"What sort of work?" I asked, having no idea of what it was like.

"Coopering," he said in a matter-of-fact way.

"What?" I asked in surprise, thinking he said that to turn me away. "Coopering, is it? I can't do that."

"Don't worry, Paddy," he said, so eager to give me the job that I felt he was afraid I might rush for the door and escape like a frightened cat before he had time to explain matters. "We'll show you how to do it."

"God bless us," I said, "I'm afraid I'm gone beyond the age of learning now as far as barrel-hooping goes."

"It's quite simple," he said. "You may as well give it a try. You can't go wrong."

I was taken overground with astonishment. I could not understand the position. When I started in the painting trade I was afraid my ignorance would prevent me getting a job, so I wanted to hide it as much as possible; but here I was now, after openly telling the Manager that I knew nothing about coopering, and he actually using all the English blarney he could think of so as to get me to start!

"Well indeed, Sir," said I, "by all means I'll give it a try since you're so willing to let me, but I'm telling you fair and square that I know absolutely nothing about the trade beyond the fact that barrels are made with hoops and staves!"

"Come along to-morrow anyhow," said he, "and see what you can do."

"The Saints in Paradise be praised," said I, "for wonders never cease. Here you are now, a man of the world, forcing me into a trade like a sheep into a dancing-master, and I after spending seven years and four in Ireland before the war in search of anything to suit me at a distance from the spade, and failing, always failing in the object of my quest!"

After spending the night waking up and laughing at the topsy-turvy way the world was going for me, I arrived at the pulping station the following morning and, after handing in my cards at the office, was taken to the workshop. The old cooper was still there but was to leave in a few days' time to take up a better job elsewhere. He was to show me what to do in the meantime.

Knowing from previous experience what a success I made of posing as a plumber, I was enjoying myself at the idea of turning up again and posing as a cooper. There were several barrels standing about with the top hoops and covers off. The cooper showed me how to put them on by first fitting a cover into the groove in the staves, putting on the second hoop from the top to keep the cover in position, pressing fat reeds between the verges of the cover and the grooves to make the barrel air-tight by means of a blunt chisel tapped with a hammer, then putting on the top hoops and hitting them well down. I found all this highly interesting and, as I was anxious to learn, I paid attention to everything I was told.

After putting the covers on several empty barrels however I began to wonder how the pulping people got anything into them, for the bungs were still in position. I thought these should have been struck out first from the inside before the covers were put on, so I mentioned my puzzle to the cooper.

"Bli' me, Paddy, that's easy," said he, taking up a big mallet as he spoke. "I'll show you now."

"What's the mallet for?" I asked.

"Taking the bungs out," he said to my great surprise.

"Putting them in, you mean," said I; correcting him with all the knowledge born of ignorance, in the style of teenagers, eager to teach their elders.

"You can do that with it too," said he, with praise-worthy tolerance, "but wait a tick till I show you."

He turned the barrel over on its side with the bung-stave on top.

"How do you think I get that out?" he asked with a twinkle in his eye.

"When you didn't do it before you put on the cover I suppose you'll have to put an augur through it and then draw it out," I ventured, wondering at the same time at the absence of previous augur-holes in it.

"No," he said, laughing. "See that mallet," he added, lifting it up. "That's called a 'bung flogger.' I'll soon show you how it works to get that bung out without touching it."

"What's that you're after saying?" I asked in surprise. "Without touching the bung at all, is it?" I continued, thinking of the charm-workers in Ireland long ago who were said to have the power of taking butter from a churn without ever going near it!

"Yes. Watch me," said he, hitting the mallet several times on each side of the bung so that the shock of pressure on the air in the barrel forced it out.

"Well, God bless us and save us, that beats the devil," said I, amazed at the simplicity of what he was after doing, and of course more interested than ever in the trade.

"When these barrels are cleaned by steam on the inside," he said, "you see how easy it is for pulped fruit to be poured into them."

He took me around the station and showed me the jobs I might be asked to do when he was gone and we had a very busy time indeed. As I had plenty of practise I felt, when he left at the end of the second day, that I had a fairly good grasp of the job. I consoled myself too that he did not coop me up in a barrel first, as I am told they do in the docks with all apprentices to the trade!

When he was gone however I felt the job much harder because I had to do it all myself. It was very tiring work, rolling heavy barrels of pulp from place to place. as well as loading and unloading boxes of fruit. All day I had to go about with a four-pound hammer in my hand for putting hoops on barrels as well as taking them off. I felt I could never stick the strain, so I told the manager, and he was very upset.

"You're doing the job to everyone's satisfaction," he said, "and we all want you to stay."

"It is very nice of you to say that, indeed," said I. "They were all kind to me here, but I'd never be able to stick the job, because 'tis too heavy for me."

He understood, so he very politely gave me my money and cards.

Then as I walked back to my lodgings I could not help laughing at the idea of having been chief cooper in the place even for one day, and pleasing everyone at the job as well! After that I felt I could act as Prime Minister if the need arose and perhaps govern the country to the satisfaction of everyone as well as ever Sancho Panza did on his island!

XXIV   *AMONG THE RED-COATS*

IT was early April with trees greening in the parks, gardens lovely with their beds of many-coloured tulips and other cultivated flowers. I had plenty time to admire them, being still out of work, the painting season not yet fully opened up. I had been to many a building-site for the past few months looking for a job but there were no vacancies anywhere. I was tired walking about because I was by no means as light on the feet as other Irishmen who travel from end to end of the country in search of work. There is the story of some vast contract hundreds of miles from London where the chief builders were mighty rich. How they and one of their workers managed to arrive at the site is described in verse:

> *McAlpine went by motor car*
> *And Wimpey went by train,*
> *But Paddy tramped the Great North Road,*
> *And got there just the same!*

My work was mostly confined to London and one day when I failed to find anything I walked along the avenues around the lovely lake where birds of many feathers flocked about the Park of Holy Jim. Then I went to look at Buckingham Palace across the road nearby. A fine building indeed, said I in my own mind, with golden gates and scarlet sentries keeping danger from the opening of its doors!

I looked at the big statue of Queen Victoria in the Square outside, and to my amazement saw that all the ground was red, wherever the coloured material making it had come from. I don't know geography very well, but I always thought the Red Square was in Moscow. To my further surprise I found the Square was round where I was standing! And there, in front of the Monarch's door, in brazen impudence, were two big statues at the base of Queen Victoria's; a hefty man wearing a leather apron holding a hammer, and a hefty woman on the other side holding a sickle!

"Did the Russians put up these?" I asked a man beside me.

"No," he said in evident surprise. "What makes you think that?"

"The statues are a symbol of Communism," said I, "and the Square is red."

"The statues are the result of a coincidence," said he, smiling. "They were put up when the Czar was sitting firmly on his throne, and it is merely by accident that the Square is that particular colour. You seem to see things that nobody else notices."

"Maybe I see red when it should be green," said I, thinking of my companions in the building trade and their strong leanings to Communism with its fair promises and foul deeds.

I looked across to where the golden gates were leading to the halls of majesty in the white-walled palace beyond, and then I went down the street towards the Railway Station where the great clock showed the hour of nine-thirty. The right time for the staff to be sitting in the building firms' offices, said I to myself, going to a telephone box with a pocket full of pennies to ring them.

"What can I do for you, Sir?" came the reply, with emphasis on the "Sir."

"Any vacancy for a painter, please?" I asked hopefully.

"Sorry, old boy," came the answer; "not at the moment."

"Thank you, Sir," said I, putting up the receiver and ringing another firm.

"Who's speaking, please?"

"Brian O'Shannissey of Swanley, Kent."

"Yes, Mr. O'Shannissey. Can I help you?"

"Anything doing for a painter, please?"

"Sorry, old boy; full up. In fact, we're putting some off this week."

It went on that way till I reached the end of my pennies and left the box. I had been ringing about twenty firms once a fortnight since Christmas and I soon learned that when the office people think the caller is a customer they call him "Sir" but as soon as they find he's only a painter looking for a job, the title suddenly changes to "Old Boy!" A painter at work is thought a very low-class person in society, and of course he is thought less of when he needs a job. I often noticed too that no matter how innocent a man may be when charged in court, the newspapers leave out the prefix at once, giving me the impression that people are always considered guilty until they are proved to be innocent. A justified omission might occur only when the prison authorities replace the prefix with a number!

I remember the sinking feeling that took hold of me after I had left the telephone box; the cold weather adding to the desolation when I realised that I would have to carry on without work again for heaven knows how long.

Now, however, hope came with the shining sun, bursting flowers and greening trees, so I went once more to the Westminster Labour Exchange from which I had been directed to many a nice job in the past. I expected the usual crowd waiting at the counter, but to my surprise this morning nobody was there, so it was likely that they all had found jobs.

"Well," said the clerk, lifting his head from the paper he was writing on, "what can I do for you?"

"Any vacancy for a painter, please?" I asked.

"Painter," he said, taking a card from the tray in front of him. "Where do you live?"

"Swanley, Sir," said I.

"That's a long way out," said he, looking at me in surprise. "Have you got your insurance card?"

I handed it to him, and when he had examined it he wrote something on an introduction card and handed them both to me.

"Officers' Mess, Chelsea Barracks," he said. "Do you know where it is?"

"I have an idea, Sir," said I, having learned a little about the district while I lived at Onslow Square. "Wait a minute now. Is it an institution for the fading of old soldiers?"

"No," said he, smiling. "It's a house of correction for young ones. You're thinking of Chelsea Hospital."

"Maybe so," said I, "but where is Chelsea Barracks then? Is it the Police Station?"

"No, no," he said. "You've got it all wrong. It's a big military place across the road from Chelsea Hospital. The Number Eleven bus will take you there. Ask the conductor to let you off at the end of Pimlico Road.

"Are you sure they'll let me in?" I asked, remembering an amusing moving picture I had seen some time before called "Passport to Pimlico."

"That introduction card will do the trick," he said.

After having a cup of tea in a nearby café I stepped on the bus and soon found the place I wanted. It was a big long grey block of buildings entered by an archway under a clock-tower. A man in khaki with a rifle stood near the sentry-box at the entry, and I knew that I might as well be knocking at a churchyard gate as asking anyone like him a question, for his lips were tightly sealed in army silence. I shuddered when I saw him, for I never liked guns of any sort, because they gave an armed man a most unfair advantage over others. I felt he wouldn't budge a fraction if I drew a scrubbing brush across the pupil of his eye. I was shy of asking questions also since the time I spoke to a uniformed porter at a waxy exhibition and found he was a statue! However, as I was pondering on the best thing to do, another man in khaki came out of the guard-room and asked me what I wanted. I was delighted to find he could talk like a human being, because I did not relish the idea of working all day long among a set of silent mummies if everyone was like the man that held his rifle at the gate!

"The Labour Exchange sent me to work in the Officers' Mess," said I, showing him the introduction card. "Where is it?"

"Come along," said he, "and I'll show you."

He took me through the archway, turned to the left when we reached the big square inside and pointed to another block of buildings facing us at the far end.

"That's it," said he. "A Firm from East Ham is doing the job, and you'll find another painter working there already."

As I walked along I saw lots of young soldiers about the place. They all had nervous looks on them, as if expecting an attack at any time, turning their heads this way and that, wondering from what new direction the enemy might open fire. I was getting nervous myself by the time I reached the door of the Officers' Mess and met the other painter who was a sharp-faced soft-spoken Welshman. He told me where to find the Manager of the Firm and after having given up my cards I returned to work with him.

After going into the hall I looked about me. Lord be praised, it was a grand place. To the right I could see the dining-room with shining table-tops and silver-ware; great chandeliers hanging from the ceiling and costly purple curtains by the windows.

Several soldiers stood about watching the workmen lay a carpet on the floor of the hall, and as I looked along the corridor to the left I saw a man wearing a dark suit and bowler hat come out of one room and go into another. After a time a second man appeared, dressed exactly the same. He stood for a few minutes in the corridor and I was astonished to see a third man in the same type of clothing come down the stairs and talk to him. It amused me to see how much alike they all looked.

"Tell me this," said I to a rather pleasant-faced soldier standing beside me, "who are the men in black? Are they grown-up Teddy Boys?"

"You'll find they're not," he said with a laugh.

I soon found that they were all officers, wearing regulation mufti, and it was not fear of attack that made the soldiers turn their heads in all directions as they crossed the square, but fear that they might miss seeing the men with the bowler hats and neglect to give the necessary salute!

The soldier I spoke to was actually an officer wearing battle-dress, but how was I going to know? His name was Captain Crossley. A few days later he passed me by in plain clothes, lifted his bowler politely, and asked if I had seen any more Teddy Boys!

The bowler was such a symbol of authority in this place that I felt if I took one around the square on top of a stick, I would be sure of many honours and salutes from soldiers!

The painting here was pleasant enough; first washing walls, then putting on whatever colour in paint the Army wanted. Each officer had a room to himself and before we went to work there, the soldiers removed the furniture, so that we got to know many of them. In the Mess the officers were nice to talk to, but outside they were very reserved. They were nearly all young fellows from nineteen to twenty-five, and by their accents, seemed to be mostly the sons of the upper classes, but apart from that, they did not appear in any way more intelligent than the soldiers who were so much concerned about saluting them. There were a few witty fellows among them however, and they played games occasionally when they came in to see how we were getting on with our work. I noticed that many of them got lots of invitations to parties, and so forth. Their batmen arranged the invitation cards on the mantel-shelves as Englishwomen do with Christmas Cards. One officer, a nice-looking gentle-mannered fellow of about twenty, had more cards than all the others. Lady This would like the pleasure of his company at the coming of age of her daughter, the Honourable Katharine So and So; The Countess of That would be pleased if he could attend on some similar occasion. I could well understand his popularity, but wondered how in the name of goodness he managed to attend to all his calls. One day he and another officer came into the room where we were working, and I commented on the big number of cards he had.

"He's the most popular man in London," said his companion with a sly smile.

"I can well believe that," said I.

"I get a few cards myself too," he added, "but my batman is too lazy to put them on the mantel-shelf."

"I'll tell you what's puzzling me," said I. "How in the name of the devil does he find time for visiting all these grand people?"

"Very simple," said his witty companion. "He doesn't go near them at all. That's why they like him so much!"

Now and again between working bouts we had an odd look out on the square. Sometimes I saw a soldier running along with a bucket in his hand and another running after him, shouting: "Left, right; left, right; mark time; about turn; about turn; quick march;" and off again like the hammers of hell.

"The Lord keep trouble from us all," said I to the Welsh-man, with fear in my eyes, "what's wrong with them?"

"Not much," he said, quite casually. "The man with the bucket is a prisoner doing his punishment. The other is the Provo putting him through it."

"Holy Patrick," said I, "what is he after doing? Did he kill somebody or what?"

"Oh no," said he, laughing; "nothing like that. He might have gone on parade with a button open on his tunic, or a piece of boiled egg stuck to the side of his jaw."

"Heavens almighty then," said I with a frown, "why are they killing the poor gorsoon for trifling things like that?"

"Discipline, my boy," said he. "Army discipline."

I saw so much of this going on day after day, that in the end I felt it was really being overdone. When I saw the Provo racing the prisoner around the square I called it the "Weasel and Rabbit" punishment, and every chance I got of talking to the officers I tried to persuade them to stop it. I ridiculed the method, and said it was no credit to the British Army; but I'm afraid I got nowhere with my argument. I also pleaded for the prisoners with the Provo Sergeant who was a friend of mine and a decent fellow, but he said he had to carry out his orders.

The easiest man in the place to talk to was the Commanding Officer. He seemed the humblest man there, and had a friendly talk with the painters whenever he met them.

Most of the private soldiers hated the Army and were look-ing forward eagerly to the day of their discharge. I got to know a lot of them, so they told me how they felt about it.

"Three weeks more to go, Paddy," one would say when he met me on my way to dinner.

"Eleven days," another would whisper as he passed me in the corridor.

While painting in the same corridor I went in to use the urinal branching from it.

"I shouldn't use that," said the Catering Sergeant. "Use the one downstairs."

But when I went in to paint it, nobody came to stop me. I said so to Captain Crossley, adding that I had often used lavatories in better places, for I knew he could see my meaning when I told him about the palaces I had worked in.

I found Chelsea Barracks the worst place I had ever come across in England for class distinction, not confusing that with the necessary differences in Army ranks, but from the ordinary social point of view.

I had been there a few months now and the weather was lovely. The soldiers were wearing their beautiful bright red uniforms and big black bearskin hats. It was a grand sight to see them on parade. What I enjoyed best of all was the band of the Scots Guards, playing the Highland Pipes up and down the square, for it brought back the memories of long ago more than any of the other bands that played there for ceremonial purposes.

When most of the officers' rooms were done we went to paint the married quarters. Here we were treated very generously by the soldiers and their families who gave us tea, morning and evening. Even when we worked in empty houses, the Provo Sergeant's wife, Mrs. Ford, sent her son Bruce with tea and cake to us. The same Bruce was a great playboy, always up to tricks, but never hurting anyone. His father used to tell me off on the square with sham discipline as if I were a soldier; then warn me to call for tea on my way home! I learned more about the British Army in this job than ever I did before, and indeed I must say I met some very fine types of men in it as well. They were a very nice sociable set of fellows. I worked for eight months among them and that was the longest time I ever stayed on any painting job. Though they all wore coats of red, their dormitories were painted green!

There was a strike on the Railway at this time so when the trains stopped running I found it very hard to get to London from Swanley. I had to get up there somehow or other, so I decided to look for a place to stay near the job for the time being. I found a Salvation Army Hostel where I was admitted and shown my bed. It was in the middle of a vast dormitory among four lines of beds arranged in perfect order from end to end. Everything looked nice and clean except the residents who came in one by one wearing dusty faded torn garments and beardy faces as the night came down.

I took off my clothes, folded them neatly, laid them under my pillow and went into bed, worried about the safety of my boots in case a thief came prowling along while I was asleep, but not knowing what to do with them and being ashamed to wear them under the blankets! I watched each resident come in. They all went quietly to their beds but continued to talk in low tones for a long time; being told off for doing so by an Irishman whose loud gruff voice was worse than any other.

It was growing late now and all the beds were filled except the one on my left, but about midnight a silent figure came slowly along and took possession of it. Although it was made down perfectly as far as I could see, he was going to take no chances with it. Perhaps he was after being the victim of dormitory tricks in the past, so he examined the ends to see if the iron joints were in position, and finding them safe enough he took each blanket and sheet away in turn, then replaced them one by one in his own way, smoothing out the sides and corners with the care a carpenter would give the planing of a door. The laying down of that bed got such attention that I should not be at all surprised if he finished it off with a spirit level! The great heat of the night kept me awake, so I had plenty time for watching.

He began to unbutton his clothes at last and I was thinking what a terrible pity it was that he should get into that bed at all and spoil the work of art, when he suddenly sat on it and took off his boots. Taking off his clothes, he laid them carefully under his pillow and smoothed it over with many delicate touches.

Well, said I in my own mind, he's finished at last. But he was not, for he stooped down, picked up his boots and went to the top of the bed. He paused for a while and blew out the long loud lip-shaking breath of a tired man. I thought he was going to put the boots under the pillow with his clothes! But he did not. Instead, he lifted up the end of the bed and put one of his boots under each leg!

So much for your sneering, Brian, said I in my own mind. He's after showing you quietly that there's method in his madness after all, and the devil mend you now! I stuffed the end of the sheet into my mouth to control the laughing as I saw him get under the blankets at last.

Then, having learned my lesson I brooded on it for a while and rather than appear barefoot on parade at Chelsea Barracks the following morning, I got up, found my boots and shod my own bed in the same way!

XXV   *FINISHING UP IN A MANSION*

PAINTING is a very dreary job at times, and when I got tired of it I usually took time off and went to see places such as the Cathedral cities of Winchester, Salisbury, Wells and Canterbury. Being interested in learning, I also visited Eton and Harrow. When I spoke to the college boys I was surprised to find that they understood every word I said, in spite of my Kerry brogue. I had no trouble in knowing what they said either, for they spoke a beautiful plain language with a lovely refined accent. The children of the working classes, on the other hand, were brought up listening to slang, and neither they nor I could understand each other at times. Their people sneered at college talk and called it "la de daw," thinking it was simply put on, and not at all natural.

Once I went to York, Melrose and Lindisfarne; then to Rievaulx, Fountains and Ripon where the jovial man who blew the Curfew Horn asked me to send him an Irish turkey for Christmas!

Things did not always go smoothly in these wanderings however because trains and buses did not run in time to take me to all the places I mapped out for my tours. Once on returning to Durham, after an interesting trip to Jarrow-on-Tyne, I was too late to find a room in the hotels, except at a very expensive one which I could not afford, so I decided on looking for a boarding house instead. All these were full as well, so what was I to do? It was far too cold to stay out all night, for a sharp breeze swept along the river as I went to and fro across the bridge in search of shelter. I knew the people of Durham were kind-hearted. I could see that from the way they treated their policemen. It was the only place I had ever seen one being allowed to sit while directing traffic. As if that was not enough, these kind people went a step further in their enlightened ideas for the prevention of cruelty to policemen, by actually building a glass canopy over him as well. So how could anyone expect to be left out in the cold in such a benevolent city! I was not either, for I asked a man standing on the bridge if he knew of any place where I might get shelter. Yes, he muttered, he would try to get me to such a place if I went with him. From the description he gave me, I thought it must be some sort of hostel, and it gave me hope in any case. As we went along we met a well-dressed fellow that I took to be a plain-clothes policeman. My friend spoke to him, and as far as I could gather he said it would be all right for him to take me to the place concerned. Being arrested as a suspect at the time would have been comfort in itself to save me from the cold; and I thought of the Irishman who once consoled himself in the lock-up that it was a good thing for him to be away from a nagging wife even for one merciful night!

We came to the building concerned at last, and it looked like a hostel all right. The porter received me kindly. Yes, he said, there was a vacancy; so after giving a few shillings to the man who brought me along, I parted with him and went in.

I gave my name and address and while it was being written I looked around me, but could not make out what kind of a place it was, because it looked neither like a Rowton House nor a Salvation Army Hostel. I concluded that it must be at least some place of refuge peculiar to the north of England for travellers like myself, in keeping with the sentry-box the policeman sat in, that looked like a big egg-timer, though used as a traffic-timer instead! To tell the plain truth I did not mind at the time whether it was a jail or an asylum, as long as I could find a comfortable bed there, so I can assure you I did not bother asking questions.

When the porter had taken a small fee with my particulars he called to someone in another room. An old man came out wearing a grey woollen suit under a wrinkled face and silvery hair. The porter told me to follow him, so in the dim light the old man led me into a long two-storey building at the back.

"I'll show you where to sleep first," he said, taking me upstairs to a big dormitory containing thirteen beds with bare mattresses covered in shiny black oilcloth, and no bed-clothes to be seen anywhere.

Half a loaf is better than no bread, said I to myself, thinking that perhaps I was to lie in my clothes all night on which-ever bed I liked best; and the dear knows there was little to choose between them, for they were as much alike as crows.

"I'll bring you the blankets," said the man in grey, disturb-ing my thoughts and putting me at ease as well. "But first of all," he added, "I must show you where to leave your clothes."

"My clothes, is it?" said I in surprise, for the room looked big enough to contain the uniforms and kits of the Durham Light Infantry, not to mind the few old rags I had on me! "Can't I leave them here?"

"No," he said with a frown. "The regulations won't allow it," and I thought perhaps the next move would be towards the fumigation box!

He took me downstairs into a small room which had rows of hot pipes laid in the order of seats along the walls about a foot from the ground.

"When you take off your clothes," he said, with the self-confidence of a sheep-dog rounding up a helpless lamb, "put them on these pipes to keep warm during the night. I'll go off and get the blankets. Leave your boots underneath and then you can go to bed as soon as you're ready."

"Naked, is it?" I asked, embarrassed at the idea of travel-ling like Adam along the corridor within a stone-throw of the Shrines of Holy Cuthbert and the Venerable Bede!

"No," he said with a dry laugh. "Keep your shirt on."

Keep your hair on, Brian, if you can, said I in my own mind, for the Lord between us and harm, these Durham people have such funny customs that maybe I'll be lucky if they don't skin me altogether! I took off my boots and clothes and left them as directed. Then as I went through the door-way and up the stairs I thought of the nightmare I used to have long ago when I was going to school; finding myself

213

like Peter Pan in Kensington Gardens, walking up the main street of Gurthagreenane with nothing on me but a shirt! I reached the dormitory in safety however and found the blankets lying on a bed before me; but I saw nobody since I came in only the old man.

"The saints protect us," said I in my own mind, "maybe I'm in the fairies at last. Heavens above," I added with a start, "my bed is Number Thirteen!"

I counted the twelve other beds to make sure, and then I looked at the blankets, wondering what to do.

"No," said I with indignation. "I'm damned if I'm having this. 'Tis bad enough being made to walk around without my clothes but they're not going to make me sleep in a bed of evil fame as well! Number Thirteen! Not if Helen of the Greeks herself was there before me!"

Then without a word I lifted up the bedclothes and spread them carefully on another bed for safety. After having knelt and said a few short prayers, I slid in under the blankets, and as a help to sleep began counting the beds around me.

"Holy Patrick, Brigid and Columbkille!" said I, breathless with amazement and anger. "I'm after being had again! Twelve beds left over a second time and I still left to lie in the thirteenth! Who ever heard of twelve black beds in a room any more than twelve black sheep in a flock! The Lord save us, I suppose this is some place like the Rowan Tree Mansion where Fuan MacCool and his companions got caught long ago and found themselves tied to the floor by the skin of their backs! Like this, there was only one door to that room too, and there was a standing order among the men of old Fuan never to enter such a place. They made the mistake however like myself, and like them I would have to suffer the consequences!

What will I do now? I asked myself as Dan O'Mahoney did when Pat Mulloy found him sitting in a leaking boat and pushed it into deep water in the lake at Gougane Barra. I wonder now, I added, if these clever Durham people have taken my clothes so that the skin of my back may stick all the better to their enchanted beds! Ah! Now I know why that policeman sits like a hatching hen on the seat of his egg-timer! The blinking man can't stand, for he's tied down!

I soon decided on upsetting their magic by every means in my power by throwing one of the beds out of the window to get rid of the unlucky number. I dare not do that however in case some other wanderer might have it booked already, and maybe claim the one I was in when he could not find it.

I was in the devil's own fix and didn't know what to do with either myself or the beds until finally I concluded that if I went on discussing with myself I would not get a wink of sleep. That was a sensible way of looking at it, so after waiting for another little while to see if anyone else came in to share my fate, and finding that nobody did, I got up, put out the light and went back to bed again.

After praying to God for protection from the powers of darkness and the Druids of Durham, I thought of what happened to my brother Murty long ago when he tried to be too clever for the rest of us by getting up in the middle of the night to have a good feed from some of the things he could not get during the day. He stirred up the fire, put on the kettle, went to the hen-house, brought in an egg and put it on to boil. Eggs were only a ha'penny each at the time, but King George was Emperor of half the world, and his image on a copper meant much more than it does now. Every egg had to be carefully watched, and they were only rarely seen on tables, save by tinkers who collected them for charity. When Tinker Dan and Mary Anne stayed for the night in a farmer's house, he was astonished when Mary Anne got up and went out saying: "I must get a couple of eggs for Dan's breakfast!" She got them easier than the farmer did. Anyhow when Murty had his tea ready he took a slice of bread and began to eat it, at the same time taking a spoon to crack his egg. To his astonishment however he could not break the shell, so he hit it again much harder, though fearing that the noise might wake the rest of us, but there was still no sign of breaking. His conscience began to pinch him then. It was wrong, he thought, to be after boiling an egg in the quiet like that! No wonder it refused to let him eat it! He was thinking of trying a hammer on it when he got second thoughts, dropped it suddenly on the table like a red hot coal, for he concluded that the devil himself must be in it surely, and with that he ran back to bed with the fright of the world in his heart, keeping the bedclothes over his head till the sun was well out in the morning! When my mother got up she was surprised to see the lamp still lighted, which was a big offence in itself on account of wasted paraffin oil, and the table still laid with an unfinished meal on it. Looking closer she saw lying beside the bread-plate, the china nest-egg used for fooling hens! She knew the fairies had not laid the table, and said nothing about it at the time, but she had a good laugh when years afterwards Murty told her what was after happening.

It is amazing how we can sometimes let our imaginations run away with us in strange places and awkward situations. I was thinking so much about this that I never felt the sleep coming over me at last, and when I woke, the sun was beaming through the windows. Realising where I was, I looked around to see if anyone else was after coming in while I was asleep, but the other beds were still empty. I stayed under the blankets for a little while before deciding what to do, which was finally nothing more exciting than to get up and put on my clothes, heaving a sigh of relief that I was not tied to the bed after all. Decisions are one thing however, and I got a shock to find I had no clothes to put on! I felt between the devil and the deep sea. What was I to do? I was still under the blankets in spite of all my intentions. Would I get up or stay in bed? I suppose I was about an hour twisting and turning before I finally lost patience with myself in such a shaky situation and got out on the boards. I opened the door and looked out. There was nobody in the corridor. Everything was as silent as the grave; a frightening lonely silence; so I bolted along and down the stairs to the room where I had left my clothes. I was surprised to find four or five others there before me; some in their shirts, some half dressed. Where did they sleep in this mysterious building? I asked myself. Bundles of shabby clothes were lying like mine on the pipes.

As I got into my trousers in a hurry I glanced at the men around me. They were a doleful-looking lot, indeed: men of the roads; unwashed, unshaven, poorly shod, wearing dusty, torn and much wrinkled garments. Their ages varied from about twenty-five to sixty, and they moved about in a quiet unearthly silence, but when I asked when breakfast would be ready they were quick enough to answer. They led me to the dining-room after I had put on my boots. I sat at a table with others who were helping themselves to mugs of tea and slices of bread and dripping. The man in grey was there too and seemed to be presiding over the catering.

"That's your breakfast," he said courteously, handing me a pint mug of tea with two slices of bread and dripping on a plate. I did not care much for the fare, so I offered one slice to the man beside me. He took it eagerly, for it seems he had a much bigger appetite than mine. When I had finished I stood up and told him I was going.

"You can't go yet," said he, to my great surprise.

"Why not?" I asked, again becoming alarmed at the idea of being kept a prisoner in a mansion of coal-black beds and dripping breakfasts.

"You must wait till you get the money," said he, "according to the rules."

That sounded highly interesting, for if he said "You can't go till you pay the money" I could understand, but now that the situation was getting comic again, I began to feel like Alice in Wonderland as I sat down to find out more about it.

"What money do you mean?" I asked.

"They give you money here," he said, "to help you on to the next place."

"That's very nice of them indeed," said I, thinking how kind the Durham people were after all, though somewhat suspicious that the money might be in the nature of "The Saxon Shilling" recruiting officers used to give to people long ago as a bait for getting them into the army; and I certainly had no desire to join any army with uniforms like those around me!

I stayed where I was for a while holding counsel with myself as to what I should do, and as the Irish are after making a name for themselves in the line of jail-breaking, I decided to try my hand at the game too, before things got any worse. I slipped away from my companions and began to edge my way towards the gate. To my surprise I got there without the least trouble and then, as a matter of courtesy I went into the lodge to say good-bye and thank the officials for their kindness in letting me in for the night. I felt this to be the safest course in any case before a sentry stopped me with a rifle at the gate saying "Where do you think you're off to?"

"Will it be all right for me to go now, Sir?" I asked the porter after he had received me kindly in the office.

"Oh, yes," he said with a friendly air. "Certainly; and call again whenever you're about."

"Thank you, Sir," said I with secret relief, "but before I go will you tell me the name of this hostel?"

"Hostel!" he said, slapping his hand over his heart, lifting his eyebrows and staring at me in surprise. "Kiddin' me now, Paddy, eh? This is no hostel."

Once more I was astonished and frightened. I began to lose confidence as I thought of Sweeney Tod, the Demon Barber; Burke and Hare, the corpse-providers; as well as expecting a secret trap-door to open under my feet and drop me into the Chamber of Horrors!

"If it isn't a hostel then," said I in desperation, holding on to the handle of the door for safety, "what the blazes is it?"

"Hostel, your eye, Paddy," said he with a hearty laugh. "This is the Durham Workhouse!"